REFINING OF OILS AND FATS

REFINING OF OILS AND FATS

FOR EDIBLE PURPOSES

A. J. C. ANDERSEN, M.Sc., F.R.I.C., M.I.Chem.E.

ACADEMIC PRESS INC., PUBLISHERS - NEW YORK

PERGAMON PRESS LTD - LONDON

1953

Published in Great Britain by Pergamon Press Ltd.,
2, 3 & 5, Studio Place, London, S.W.1.

U.S.A. edition published by Academic Press Inc., Publishers,
125 East 23rd Street, New York, N.Y.

Printed in Great Britain by Adlard & Son, Ltd., Bartholomew Press, Dorking.

CONTENTS

PREFACE

THIS work was originally planned as the section on Refining of Oils and Fats in a contemplated up-to-date English edition of Dr. H. SCHOENFELD's well-known handbook *Chemie, Technologie und Verwendung der Fette und Oele*, published in Vienna in 1937. The untimely death of Dr. SCHOENFELD in 1951 caused the project to be abandoned, but as the manuscript of this contribution was well in hand the publishers decided to issue it as a separate book. The author wishes to record his indebtedness to Dr. SCHOENFELD for much helpful advice on selection of material and for information from his wide knowledge of, particularly, the Continental industry and practice.

His thanks are also due, and herewith expressed, to a number of Companies, who have generously placed at his disposal information and drawings of plant, particularly the Alfa-Laval Company Ltd., Brentford, Middlesex; Bamag Limited, London; The Dorr-Oliver Company Ltd., London; The Foster Wheeler Company, London; W. J. Fraser and Co. Ltd., Dagenham, Essex; The Fuller's Earth Union Ltd., Redhill, Surrey; The Girdler Corporation, Louisville, U.S.A.; Messrs. S. H. Johnson and Co. Ltd., London; and Sharples Process Engineers Limited, London.

He also acknowledges with thanks permission by The Institution of Chemical Engineers, London, to reproduce illustrations 83 and 85 from the Institution's *Transactions*, Vol. 27 (1949), pages 106 and 109.

This book gives no detailed information of the methods of analyses used in the refining of fats and oils. Readers who seek this might consult the following books:

K. A. WILLIAMS. *Oils, Fats and Fatty Foods*. J. & A. Churchill Ltd. London, 1950.

T. P. HILDITCH. *The Industrial Chemistry of the Fats and Waxes*. Baillière, Tindall and Cox. London, 1949.

G. S. JAMIESON. *Vegetable Fats and Oils*. Reinhold Publishing Corporation. New York, 1943.

Official and Tentative Methods of the American Oil Chemists' Society. Chicago, 1946.

British Standards Specification 684, 1950. *Methods of Analyses of Oils and Fats*.

THE AUTHOR.

INTRODUCTION

MOST crude oils and fats, whether obtained by pressing, solvent extraction or rendering, are given a preliminary cleaning and clarification treatment by settling, screening, filtration or centrifugation to make them more resistant against deterioration during storage. When required for edible purposes they are nearly always given a further refining treatment; when intended for technical non-edible purposes they also frequently need some treatment to remove impurities, degradation products or undesirable constituents which would interfere with their use.

Animal fats intended for human consumption, such as beef suet and lard, by selection of the raw material and by appropriate methods of rendering can be obtained of such a quality and purity as to make them directly suitable for consumption. Similarly some vegetable oils, for instance, olive oil, when derived from fresh fruit pressed at low temperature, the so-called virgin oil, can also be used without further treatment, although settling and straining is often used. Cacao butter, as obtained by pressing from freshly roasted beans, is another fat which is mostly used without further refining.

In most cases, however, some refining treatment must be applied, depending on the nature of the impurities and undesirable constituents and on the purposes for which the fat is required.

The impurities may be of the following types:

1. Fat-insoluble particles dispersed in the fat.
2. Material held in colloidal suspension in the fat.
3. Fat-soluble substances.

The fat-insoluble impurities can be removed by mechanical means, such as settling, filtration or centrifugation ; they consist principally of seed or tissue particles, mucilage, fibres from press-cloths, dust, mineral matter, traces of moisture, etc.

The material held in colloidal suspension or solution consists largely of phosphatides (cephalin and lecithin), carbohydrates, mucilage and protein, often complex compounds of these, and can be removed by treatment with steam, water, electrolytes, followed by settling, centrifugation or filtration with adsorbents or other filter aids.

The fat-soluble compounds are primarily free fatty acids, derived together with small amounts of mono and diglycerides from the hydrolysis of triglycerides, colouring matters, such as carotenoids, chlorophylls and others not yet fully known, oxidation and decomposition products, ketones and aldehydes which frequently have an unpleasant taste and odour, sterols, hydrocarbons, resins and various so far unidentified substances. Some crude oils also contain some toxic or harmful compounds, for instance,

1

gossypol in cottonseed oil, and some contain traces of sulphur compounds, as for instance the isothiocyanic acid ester of allyl alcohol in rapeseed oil and mustard seed oil.

Many of these substances must be removed before the fat is suitable for use, even for technical purposes. Quantitatively the most important impurity is free fatty acids, and although a small percentage, about 0·5 per cent of free acids with sixteen or more carbon atoms in the chain do not unfavourably affect the flavour of carefully prepared animal fats, such as high-grade beef suet and lard, or low-temperature produced vegetable oil from selected fruit and seed, such as olives and groundnuts, a thorough elimination of the free fatty acids is necessary in most fats and also helps to reduce the cost of removing other undesirable constituents.

The methods used and the degree to which fats have to be refined depend on the usage to which the treated fats are to be put. When required for edible purposes it is important that all constituents which give an unpleasant taste and odour and an unattractive colour are removed. For some edible purposes a white completely bleached fat is desired, for others a pale yellow or butter-yellow colour is satisfactory. Where artificial colouring of fats is required, the residual original colour in the fat must be limited to one that will not interfere with the aim of the artificial colour.

Oils for varnishes and lacquers must, even when cold, be free from turbidity and suspensions which would affect unfavourably the clarity of the coating films, and for oil-lacquers only pale or colourless oils can be used. Thus the crude drying oils, intended for boiled oils or stand-oils, must be thoroughly clarified, de-slimed and bleached. For the manufacture of good soaps a suitable pretreatment of the crude fats is necessary, and the preparation of palm and sanctuary oils includes an intensive de-sliming of the crude oils.

In connection with the refining of fats and oils for edible purposes it should be mentioned that whereas in the United States of America the term "refining" is applied to the operations of pre-treatment and de-acidification or neutralization in most other countries it means the complete series of treatments, including also bleaching and deodorization, to make the fat suitable for edible use.

REMOVAL OF FAT-INSOLUBLE IMPURITIES

BEFORE crude fats are stored the fat-insoluble impurities should be removed as a protection against deterioration. Fragments of oil seeds and cell tissues contain fat-splitting enzymes, lipases, which in the presence of even traces of moisture cause hydrolysis of the glycerides with the formation of steadily increasing amounts of free fatty acids. Furthermore, seed fragments and coagulated mucilage provide with moisture a fertile breeding ground for micro-organisms, some of which may cause splitting of the glycerides and other types of rancidity, putrefaction and development of objectionable odours and taste. As fats and oils, to keep them fluid, are generally stored at temperatures which are suitable for intensive enzymic and microbial activity, the need for the removal of these insoluble impurities is obvious.

The effect on quality of purification before storage has often been demonstrated; for instance JAMIESON and BAUGHMAN[1] found that cottonseed oil, obtained by hot pressing and stored at 19°C for seven months without prior filtration, showed an increase in acid value from 4·24 to 5·65. Filtered oil, stored under similar conditions, increased in acidity from 4·24 to 4·4 only.

The presence of these insoluble impurities also tends to increase the losses in subsequent refining.

The principal methods for removing suspended fat-insoluble impurities are (a) Settling, (b) Filtration and (c) Centrifugation.

CLARIFICATION OF CRUDE FATS BY SETTLING

This method is lengthy and not very effective. Settling of the finely suspended particles proceeds very slowly, and a sharp separation of the precipitate, generally called "foots," and the supernatant fat is difficult to achieve. As crude fats frequently contain up to 0·5 per cent moisture, most of which settles with the solid impurities, conditions for incipient deterioration by enzymes and micro-organisms are very favourable. Rapid development of free fatty acids takes place in the fat occluded in the foots, and these, together with the objectionable flavours, arising from bacterial activity, contaminate the upper layers of fat and reduce its value. Although apparently simple, the method is rather expensive and ineffective. Removal of the upper layer of fat by decantation or the lower layer of foots by draining causes disturbance in the contact layer, and some foots get back into the clarified fat. An absolutely clear fat can rarely be obtained, with the result that further treatment by filters or centrifuges may be necessary.

Settling tanks can be divided by vertical partition walls into several compartments. In this way disturbance caused by the inflow of fat can be limited to the first compartment, while the fat is quiescent in the following sections. The clarified fat can be drawn off through cocks at different levels or through adjustable swivel skimmer pipes. Fat can be recovered from the residual foots by means of centrifuges.

Cylindrical or square tanks with dished, conical or pyramidal bottoms are also used. As it is necessary to keep the fat in liquid condition, means of heating must be provided, either by placing the tanks in warm rooms or by fitting them with heating jackets or coils, the former being preferred, as coils, though cheaper to install, may interfere with complete settling.

FILTRATION

A more modern, rapid and effective method for removing suspended impurities is filtration. The fluid mixture of fat and solid impurities is pressed through a filter material, which retains the solids while the liquid passes through. Filter materials may be textiles of cotton, wool, artificial fibres, fine-meshed wire netting, or special filter aids, such as asbestos, kieselguhr, processed diatomaceous earth (Filtercel), etc.

At various stages in course of the refining operations fats are filtered once or several times under varying conditions, and as the principles and plants are similar to those for purification of crude oils, the more important arrangements and constructions of filtration plants and their operation in refineries will be mentioned here.

The most important type is the *Filterpress*, which consists of a number of plates of filter surfaces so designed that when they are pressed together closed spaces or chambers, capable of resisting internal pressure, are formed between adjacent plates, into which the fat with the suspended solids is pressed. Cloth or other filtration material covers the filter surfaces and permits the passage of the clear fat, while the sediment is retained in the hollow space between the surfaces and builds up the so-called presscake which when filtration is finished is removed by opening the press.

Fig. 1 shows a filterpress, consisting of a number of suitably shaped plates *P* which are inserted between strong head and end plates *K* and *L* and covered with filter cloths. The head plate *K* is fixed whereas the end plate *L* is movable, and like the intermediate plates *P* can slide on and be supported by guide rails or bars *T*. The whole system of plates can be pressed tight together by means of a strong central screw *S* with handwheel or ratchet tightening gear. Big presses have often a hydraulic tightening gear. When thus pressed together the press forms, as the result of the special construction of the plates *P*, a number of adjacent tightly closed, but inter-communicating chambers with the filter cloths providing the packing gaskets. The untreated material is pumped through valve *u* into the filterpress chambers and clear filtrate leaves through outlet cocks *h*. The sediment is retained in the hollow spaces between the filter cloths and gradually fills up the whole space and forms a more or less compact cake.

According to the arrangement adopted for forming the hollow spaces between the filterplates one distinguishes between (*a*) recessed plate presses (chamber presses) and (*b*) flush plate and distance frame presses (frame presses).

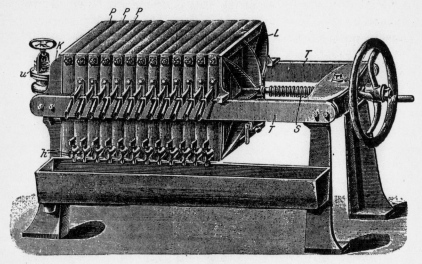

Fig. 1.   Filterpress.

Chamber Presses

In these presses the hollow space in which the residue, the filterpress cake, collects is formed by recesses on the plates which have raised rims standing up above the drainage surface on both sides of the plates. When these are placed in position chambers are formed between the plates of a depth equal to twice the depth of the recess of the plates. A hole is provided in each plate through which the material to be filtered enters the chambers, and a filter cloth hangs over each plate and is provided with a hole in each half, corresponding with the feed hole of the plate, the joint round which is made with a clip.

Fig. 2 shows a section through the head and a few chambers of this type of press with centre feed inlet. A, A_1 and A_2 are filterplates, forming chambers B, B_1 and B_2, into which the material to be filtered enters by the inlet D. The rims C of the plates are machined, so that when the plates are tightened up in position the cloths make tight joints between the plates. It will be seen that each chamber is completely lined with cloth, so that when the material to be filtered is forced under pressure into the chamber, the solid particles are retained by the cloth, whereas the liquid clarified portion, the filtrate, passes through. As the surface of the plates is grooved or studded with bosses of different shapes, channels for drainage are formed between the cloths and the bottom of the grooves, which allow the filtrate to drain to the connecting ports E, leading to the outlet cocks.

Fig. 2 illustrates three methods of fixing the cloths on the plates. F and F_1 are screwed unions, G is an instantaneous clip which is fixed by a quarter turn, and H is an adjustable hook to which cloths are attached when sewn round the centre hole.

The thickness of the rim of the plate is determined by the density and thickness of the presscake through which the filtrate can be pressed without excessive pressure. When the cakes have filled the chambers the press is

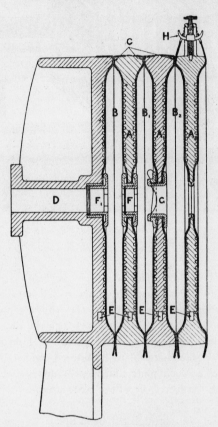

Fig. 2.   Filterpress details, Chamber Press.

unlocked, the end plate drawn back and the plates are glided along the rails or bars to open the press, which causes the cake to fall off the cloths to the floor or to a hopper underneath.

Chamber presses are particularly suitable for filtration of liquids with a small amount of solids; it is the simplest and cheapest type of filterpress, but the wear on filter cloth is heavier and the removal of cake less easy than with frame presses. These presses are mostly constructed with central feed inlet, which gives least strain on the cloths. Inlet in the top is useful with slimy material or with heavy suspensions. Bottom corner inlet enables the liquid contents to be drained out before opening the press, which is an advantage when dealing with materials that do not form a solid cake.

Fig. 3 shows different arrangements of inlets and outlets on recessed plates for chamber presses. *A* has centre inlet and cock outlet. *B* has top inlet and bip or spout outlet. *C* has bottom corner feed and cock outlet. *D* has

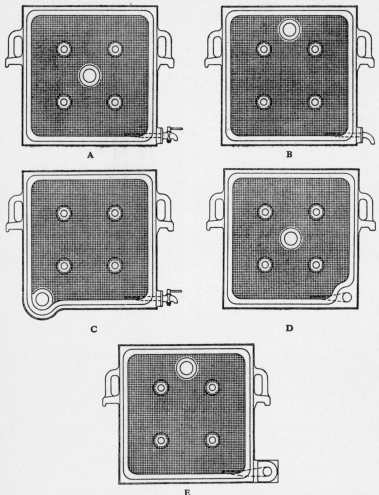

Fig. 3. Types of recessed plates (Courtesy: *S. H. Johnson & Co. Ltd.*).

centre feed and internal closed delivery outlet. *E* has top feed and external closed delivery outlet.

Frame Presses

The plates of this type of filterpress have the faced joint surfaces practically flush with the filtering surface, the chambers being formed by hollow frames, which have faced surfaces corresponding with those of the plates and are placed alternately with them. These presses are specially suitable for filtration of liquids with a high proportion of solids, particularly fat and bleaching earth, but owing to the restricted inlet ports the feed materials should be free from lumps. The inlet for the material to be filtered is through a channel running the length of the press and having ports through the frames communicating with their interior. The cloths are hung over the plates so that each chamber has a cloth on both sides.

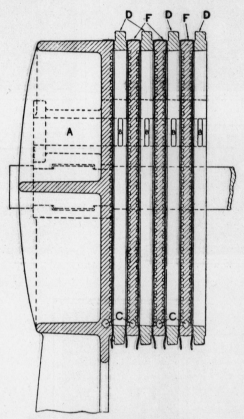

Fig. 4.   Filterpress details, frame press.

Fig. 4 shows a section through a few chambers of a frame press. F is the filterplates and D the distance frames which form the chambers. A is the inlet channel for the material, B the port connecting the channel with the interior of the chambers. The channel A is formed when the press is assembled, and when the unfiltered material is pumped into the chambers, the solids gradually build up the press cake, while the filtrate passes through the cloths and runs along the grooves or channels on the plate to the outlet ports C which communicate with the outlet cocks or bips, or discharge into a closed delivery pipe.

As with the chamber press there are a number of variations in the disposition of inlet and delivery passages, the choice depending on the nature of the material to be filtered. The passages can either be formed by eyes within the joint surfaces of the plates and frames, or in lugs external to the joint surfaces. The advantage of the latter arrangement is that no holes are

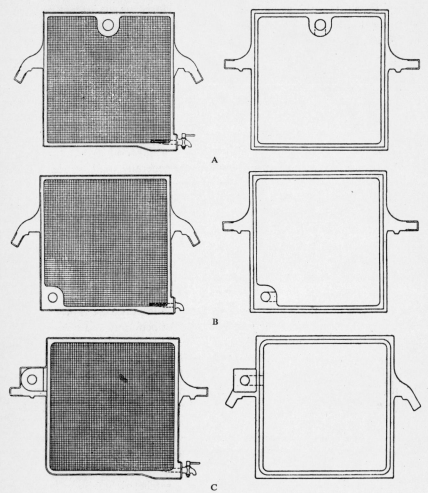

Fig. 5. Types of plates and frames (Courtesy: *S. H. Johnson & Co. Ltd.*).

required in the cloths, which can be cut in plain length, and much of the time and labour necessary to register the cloths, where these have holes corresponding with those in the plates, is saved. The tightening of the joints, where external passages are provided, can either be by independent cloth cuffs or by special collars or other packings of suitable material.

Fig. 5 shows some examples of inlet and outlet arrangements for frame presses. *A* show plate and frame arranged for internal top feed and cock

9

outlet, *B* shows corner bottom internal feed and bip outlet; *C* shows external lug feed arranged for cloth cuff packing and with cock outlet.

In both types of presses, if the delivery is by cock or bip, each plate discharges a visible stream of oil into the collecting trough, so that it is easy to detect if a cloth is damaged or otherwise permits the passage of turbid filtrate, in which case the outlet cock can be closed or the stream of turbid oil segregated by using a longitudinally divided trough and taps with swivel nosepieces.

Before opening the filled press the amount of residual oil held in the press cake may be considerably reduced by displacing it with air, steam or some suitable liquid, but such recovered material should be kept separate as it may be of inferior quality. The displacement material follows the same channels as the oil.

For the filtration of crude fats where the proportion of solid impurities is usually small, but frequently of colloidal or mucilagenous type, presses with large filter surface and small cake space are generally used, as the gummy character of the residue has a tendency to clog the pores in the cloth. It is not necessary to provide outlet cocks for each plate as there is only small risk of turbidity during filtration. Oils which by being kept cold have separated phosphatides and similar sticky colloidal compounds, and therefore must be filtered cold, are also suitably dealt with in such a press. The filtrate can in those cases be discharged through the small oil outlets from each plate into a common closed delivery channel similar to the common inlet channel for unfiltered material.

Closing the Press.—As filtration is done under pressure which may be 40–50 lb./sq. in. or more, it is essential both for economy and efficiency that the press should be capable of being properly tightened. The pressure for closing it can be applied in different ways. The press shown in Fig. 1 is closed by pressure exerted by a central mild steel screw with handwheel against the middle of a cast-iron end plate. When the press is full and filtration finished the spindle is screwed back and the end plate, and subsequently the other filterplates, drawn back on the side bars.

The gradual increase of pressure on the plates when closing the press can on heavy presses be effected by means of a spur wheel and pinion as shown in Fig. 6.

The tightening screw is often fitted with a ratchet tightening gear instead of a handwheel. This gear has a handle for running the screw backwards and forwards quickly and a lever bar for putting on the final tightening pressure (Fig. 7).

A different method of transferring the pressure to the plates is adopted on the press made by the *Railway A.G.*, Vienna (Fig. 8). The end plate is made of wrought-iron; the closure spindle, which is actuated by a spur and pinion mechanism, does not press directly on the end plate, but on two angularly placed steel connecting bars *T*, which transfer the pressure by means of a bar *K* to channel iron bars on the end plate. It is claimed that in this

10

Fig. 6. Filterpress with spurwheel closure (Courtesy: *S. H. Johnson & Co. Ltd.*).

Fig. 7. Filterpress with ratchet tightening gear
(Courtesy: *S. H. Johnson & Co. Ltd.*).

Fig. 9.   Filterpress with rotatable distance piece.

Fig. 10.   Filterpress with hydraulic tightening gear
(Courtesy: *S. H. Johnson & Co. Ltd.*).

manner more intensive pressure is put on the outer parts of the plates where this is specially required to ensure tightness.

Fig. 9 illustrates a press on which the closure is effected by a spindle actuated by spur and pinion with handwheel. A rotatable distance piece, indicated by the arrow and placed between the screw and the end plate, enables time to be saved on opening and reassembling the press. If, for instance, when opening, the screw is turned back a few turns, the distance piece can be swung out from the central position and the end plate immediately drawn back. This press is also fitted with hinged splash plates underneath; when it is in use the plates are turned horizontally to catch drops of oil that may leak from the press and drain them into a collecting tank; when the press is opened the plates are hinged back to a vertical position to permit the cakes to fall into a hopper or conveyor under the press for removal. This arrangement promotes tidiness of operation.

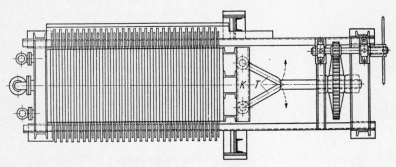

Fig. 8.   Filterpress, special closure.

Hydraulic tightening gears, which are advantageously used on large presses and in installations with a large number of presses, obviate the risk of excessive strain being put on the framework of the press, as by the provision of a small hydraulic gauge an indication can be obtained, when the correct tightening pressure has been reached. A filterpress with plate dimensions of 80 cm × 80 cm and working at pressures of about 4 atm. requires a closure pressure of about 25·6 tons. A press with hydraulic tightening gear is shown in Fig. 10. The heavy end plate is provided with a closing screw which works in a screw bush that is made in the form of a hydraulic ram working in a hydraulic cylinder carried in the back standard of the press. The hydraulic pressure in this case is obtained by a hand pump and the unit is therefore self-contained.

Other constructions make use of available high-pressure water supply and substitute for the closing screw a ram working in a hydraulic cylinder carried by the back standard of the press. The ram in this case thrusts directly on to the centre boss on the end plate.

The plates and frames of filterpresses are generally square. Round plates are occasionally used, and mostly for extraction of filterpress residues with volatile solvents or for filtration of miscellas because secure solvent-tight closure is easier to achieve. Fig. 11 shows a round filterplate from a chamber press. *A* are the supporting brackets, *B* the inlet central channel, and *C* the outlet ports to the cock.

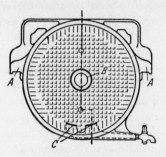

Fig. 11.   Round filterplate for chamber press.

Fitting of the Filter Cloths.—Figs. 12*a*, 12*b* and 12*c* show various ways of fitting the cloths to the filterplates. In Fig. 12*a* the cloths are folded and hung over the plates so that the holes in the cloths are opposite the inlet holes in the plates, where they are held tight by means of screw unions or

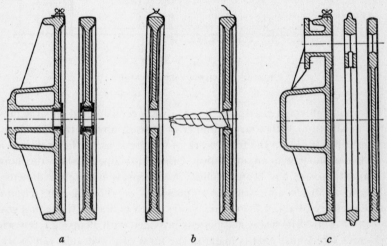

a   b   c

Fig. 12.   Fastening filtercloths.

clips. On the end plates the cloths are bent over the edge and held by wing nuts.

Fig. 12*b* shows the fitting of a pull-through cloth. This is made from two pieces which are sewn together at the central inlet to form a sleeve (see Fig. 13). One half of the double cloth is pushed through the inlet hole of the plate and the cloth is then flattened out on both sides of the plate and tied at the edges. This kind of cloth is suitable on chamber presses.

Fig. 12c shows curtain cloths for frame presses. They are hung over the plates with the openings in the cloths and the plates registering, thus giving the oil a free flow through the common inlet channel.

Filter cloths are made of cotton, linen, wool, woven wire netting, specially made cellulose material and, in recent years, plastic fibres sufficiently thermostable to withstand filtration temperatures. Cotton is usually the cheapest; wool is particularly suited for acid conditions. The mechanical strength and resistance of the cloths should be high, the weave to be determined by the performance required. An open weave may permit high speed of filtration, but is more likely to give a cloudy filtrate. Cloths and papers are often used in combination to ensure a blank filtrate.

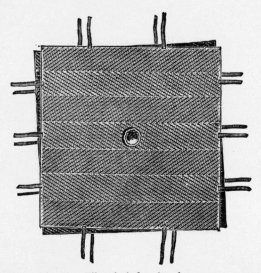

Fig. 13.   Filtercloth for chamber press.

Where the solid impurities in the oil are very small or of a colloidal mucilagenous nature, filter aids or clarifiants are frequently used. Asbestos fibres, fuller's earth, bentonite, kieselguhr, specially prepared diatomaceous earth, etc., with high adsorptive properties are used in small proportions of a fraction of 1 per cent to assist in obtaining high rates of filtration by preventing clogging of the filter surface.

Filtration Pumps.—The pressure required for supplying the oil to the presses and forcing it through the filter can be obtained by gravity, but practical considerations generally demand the use of pumps. Centrifugal pumps which give a steady stream of oil are most suitable, and provide the steadily increasing pressure required as filter resistance grows. Piston pumps with their pulsating deliveries should be fitted with air vessels for pressure equalization. The supply line to the press should be provided with a safety return valve set at the maximum permissible pressure, the return pipe leading back to the supply vessel. Filtration pressure is sometimes obtained by the pneumatic system, using one or more vessels of the Montejus type, into which the material to be filtered is first run and then displaced under pressure by compressed air.

In some arrangements the forcing pump is carried on the support for the filterpress, as shown in Fig. 6.

Filterpress Details.—Filterpresses are mostly made of cast iron. Recently some refineries have introduced electric-welded all-steel presses which with equal capacity are considerably lighter. In plants where high-grade edible fat is treated, presses sometimes have sections of stainless steel or aluminium where these come in contact with the edible fat. Wooden presses are used for special purposes, for instance on fatty acids or where the oil contains corrosive constituents.

Some filterpresses have the plate surfaces covered with fitted strainer-plates or fine-meshed wire netting against which the cloth is flattened out. Such an arrangement prevents the cloth from being pressed into the grooves on the plate. Suitable design of the pattern of the plate surface and adequate texture of the cloth obviate the need for such protection plates. This drainage surface may be designed as fine or coarse grooves, depending on the fluidity of the oil; the grooves or drain channels should be suitably clear and narrow to avoid the cloth being pressed into them; the cloths should be well supported with a minimum of dead spaces. A much favoured drainage surface is a plate studded with small bosses of the shape of truncated square pyramids, arranged regularly in evenly spaced lines (see Fig. 14); this system makes a large proportion of the cloth available for effective filtration, gives good support to the cloth, and by having both horizontal and vertical drainage channels gives free passage to the flow of the filtrate in several directions towards the outlet ducts. The surface design, as well as the edges of the filter plates, should have smooth corners to avoid severe wear on the cloth which, under pressure, is subject to heavy strain.

The capacity of a press can be reduced by the insertion of a blank or dummy plate of suitably strong construction to cut out of operation some of the chambers. For liquids with only a small proportion of solids, and where these are of such a gummy nature that they cause filtration to cease, when a thin deposit has been formed on the cloth, presses with shallow chambers are used. In chamber presses with recessed surfaces the depth of the chamber exceeds 2 in. only in very large units. In frame presses the depth of the chamber is slightly greater than the thickness of the distance frame, which is usually not less than $\frac{5}{8}$ in. and may be as much as 2–$2\frac{1}{2}$ in.

For special purposes filterpresses can be built with ducts for steam, hot water or cooling liquid to regulate the temperature of the press.

Leaf Pressure Filters

Filterpresses are rather heavy in labour charges and usage of filter cloths. To effect improvements in this direction the type of filtration plant known as the leaf pressure filter was introduced in various industries, and some

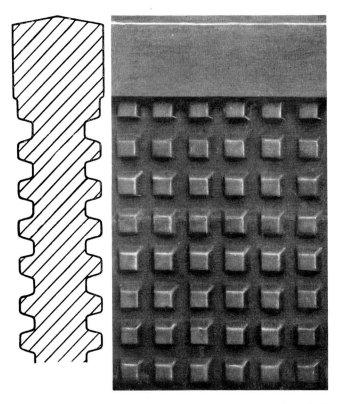

Fig. 14. Filter plate surface (Courtesy: *S. H. Johnson & Co. Ltd.*).

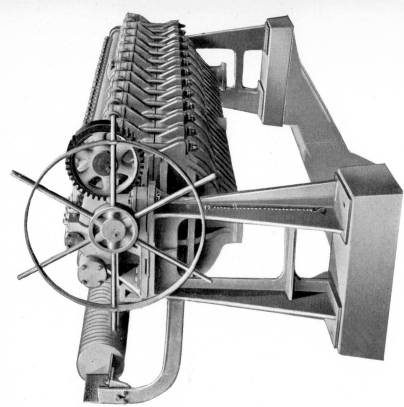

Fig. 16. Sweetland filter, closed (Courtesy: *Dorr-Oliver Co. Ltd.*).

Fig. 15. Sweetland filter, open (Courtesy: *Dorr-Oliver Co. Ltd.*).

of these filters, particularly the Sweetland press, have in recent years found many applications in the oil and fat industries.

In this press the suspended impurities are retained in an easily removable form on the outside of the filter leaves, which are mounted parallel to each other at equal distances inside a casting made in the form of a tank. This latter is designed to stand heavy pressure and is built as a horizontal cylinder, divided longitudinally in two halves, the upper and fixed half being supported on legs, while the lower half is hinged to the upper along one side and counter-balanced to facilitate opening and closing, so that the filter leaves can be exposed for cleaning. A special locking device makes it possible to open or close the filter within a fraction of a minute. Special gaskets are fitted to tighten the joint of the two halves, and a boss cast along the top half has holes to receive the outlet nipples from the filter leaves. On the inside of the upper body are spacers to keep the filter leaves in alignment. An excentric shaft on the upper half carries a number of swing bolts, which engage suitable lugs on the lower half and tighten the two halves together when the excentric shaft is turned. A special device ensures that the tightening can be adjusted along the length of the cylinder.

The filter leaves, from which the residues are removed by hinging open the lower half, or by sluicing and draining, are circular pieces of heavy wire screen, the edges of which are bound round the periphery by a U-shaped ring or similar edging; this stiffens the leaf and provides the binding for the filter cloth covering the surface of the leaf and which may be Monel or other metal cloth or, in some cases, cotton or other textiles. Each leaf has an outlet at the top, which is provided with a sight glass and shut-off cocks and discharges into a common manifold. The feed inlet is through one end of the upper body, in which a cored passage-way in the fixed casting joins with a similar coring in the lower body, terminating into a distributing channel running along the bottom of the filter. There is a drain pipe from the bottom and an air vent at the top to release air when filling the cylinder. Steam, air or wash liquor can be supplied to the cylinder via an internal manifold with nozzles to facilitate draining, drying of the press cakes or sluicing away of residue; steam and air supplied via the filtrate manifold can be used as blow-back to loosen and discharge residue from the filter surfaces.

Figs. 15 and 16 show a Sweetland press in the open and the closed positions. Fig. 17 shows a section through the press and the various pipe connections. Fig. 18 shows a longitudinal diagram of part of a press, and Fig. 19 a filter leaf with and without cover.

The screen prevents the filter surfaces from collapsing under pressure and provides the drainage area for the percolating filtrate. The outlet fitting from the screen and leaf can either connect with the top of the filter area—top drainage—or with a flattened tube reaching the lowest part of the filter area—bottom drainage—in which case more complete draining of filtrate in the screen is possible, when air or steam pressure is used to reduce the oil content of the press cake.

15

The Sweetland filter can be used with or without filter aid and for removing bleaching earth after bleaching. It is very economical with filter cloth and this is not subject to stretch, nor is it used as a gasket; hence light cloths or wire webbing can be used.

The diagrams of a cross-section, Fig. 17, and a longitudinal section, Fig. 18, of a press indicate the flow-through when the press is used for filtration of oil from bleaching earth. The liquid with suspended solids enters through the cored channel *A*, Fig. 18, at the end, and is distributed in the interior via the channel in the bottom half, which is covered by a perforated plate. The solids gradually build up cakes on the filter leaf

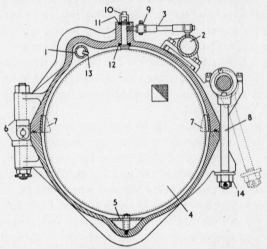

Fig. 17. Sweetland filter, cross-section.

1. Internal manifold.	6. Hinge.	11. Lead washer.
2. Filtrate manifold.	7. Side, leaf spacers.	12. Rubber washer.
3. Sight glass.	8. Swing bolt.	13. Nozzle.
4. Filter leaf.	9. Filtrate shut-off cock.	14. Swing bolt castle nut.
5. Distributing plate.	10. Cap nut.	

surfaces *D*, while the filtrate percolates through under pressure into the drainage area of the wire screen *C* and is forced out through separate outlets from each leaf at the top. The press can be drained through bottom outlets *B*. On the way to the common outlet manifold *2*, Fig. 17, the filtered oil passes a cock *9* and a sight glass *3* where it can be seen whether a filter leaf does not function efficiently. When filtration is finished, the oil content of the cake on the filter leaves can be reduced by air or steam pressure, be displaced by a detergent solution, or extracted with solvent. Finally, the residue is removed from the leaves and sluiced down with water from the internal manifold *1* with nozzles *13* and drained off.

The Kelly filter is a leaf pressure filter constructed for high-pressure filtration. Although extensively used in the mineral oil industry it is rarely employed for edible fats. It consists of a horizontal cylinder with removable end which can be clamped on tightly by a special locking device. The filter surfaces consist of a number of vertical filter leaves supported on a carriage attached to the removable head; they are run into the cylinder before filtration and afterwards withdrawn completely with the head cover for removal of the cake. The filtration principle is similar to that of the Sweetland filter leaf, each leaf having a separate outlet pipe which passes through the removable end and discharges into a common collecting pipe or trough outside. The feed pipe is at the bottom of the cylinder, which is also provided with a drain pipe.

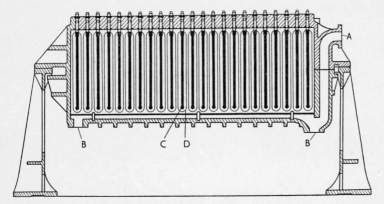

Fig. 18. Sweetland filter, longitudinal section.

A. Feed inlet.   C. Filter leaf.
B. Drainage main outlet.   D. Cake in leaf.

Leaf Matting Filters

For filtration at moderate or low pressures of turbid oils a special type of leaf filter, the so-called leaf matting filter, has found wide application, particularly for final blank filtration, "polishing", of table and salad oils.

In this filter the sediment does not come in direct contact with the filter cloth, but is adsorbed on a mat of filtration material or filter aid which prevents the compacting of the sediment. As suitable filtration aid serves a solid finely divided material, resistant against compression and distortion and having maximum particle surface; it should readily form a permeable deposit with fine capillary pores. Asbestos fibres are particularly suitable for forming the pulp matting, the fibre length being adjusted to the performance required.

The matting filters can be used in two ways: (a) The filter surfaces, which correspond to the plates in a filterpress, can first be covered with a thin layer of the filter aid before the turbid oil is submitted to filtration; the pulpy layer prevents the colloidal mucilaginous particles from penetrating into the filter cloth or wire webbing, which covers the filterplate, and causing excessive resistance to filtration. The layer also facilitates the removal of the cake after filtration. The pulp matting is the actual filtration medium. (b) A definite quantity of filter aid can be added to and mixed with the turbid oil, before it is filtered.; the filter aid increases the porosity of the cake, lowers its compressibility and reduces the resistance to filtration.

Asbestos fibre is the best filter aid for method (*a*). For method (*b*) diatomaceous earth such as kieselguhr is often used; this consists largely of pure silicic acid in very fine uniform particle size, but of complicated structure, so that it offers a large surface for adsorption of the solids; it is given a special treatment to increase the adsorptive power. Filtercel is one of the many proprietary materials of this type.

For de-gumming of linseed oil and clarification of table and salad oils the leaf matting filter of the *Seitz Works*, Bad Kreusnach, Germany, is extensively used. It consists of a metal casing in which a number of vertical

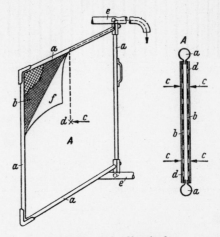

Fig. 20.   Seitz filter leaf.

filter leaves of fine wire gauze are placed side by side. From a mixing tank a mixture of oil and asbestos fibres is first pumped to the filter to build up a thin asbestos matting on the leaves. The turbid oil is then under a head of 3–4 metres run on to the filter. The sediment is held back by the asbestos layer, and when filtration is finished this layer with the sediment can be removed as a blanket. In Fig. 20, *A* is the filter element or leaf of the Seitz filter, framed by four tubes *a*, open towards the inside of the frame, over both sides of which the wire gauze *b* is stretched. The turbid oil mixed with filter aid flows under gravity or pump pressure into the casing and on to the filter surface, as indicated by *c*, and the filter aid is retained on the gauze and builds up the filtration matting *d*. The clarified liquid penetrates this layer into the filter element and flows as indicated by the dotted line, to the frame tubes *a* and is collected in the manifolds *e* leading to the filtered oil tank; *f* shows how the exhausted filter layer can be peeled off.

Fig. 21 shows a plant employing Seitz filters. *A* is a mixing vessel with stirrer for oil and asbestos. The mixture is supplied to the filter *F* by centri-

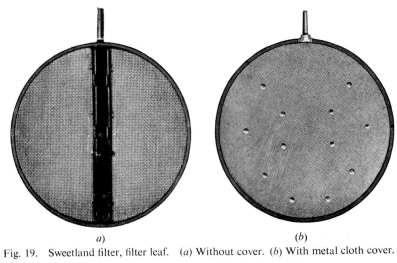

$a)$ (b)

Fig. 19. Sweetland filter, filter leaf. (*a*) Without cover. (*b*) With metal cloth cover.

Fig. 22. Rotary vacuum filter.

fugal pump *P*. When the filter matting has been built up, the turbid oil is taken from tank *H*, which is placed some metres above the filter, and run into the filter casing. F_1 is a front view of the opened filter, F_2 a section through a filter.

There are several other makes of low-pressure filters in which filter leaves are suspended or submerged in tanks and having a variety of types of filter-plates—chains, corrugated plates, wire gauze. If the plates do not consist of very fine gauze, they must be covered by a close-fitting filter bag before they are coated with filter aid.

Vacuum Filters

Continuous rotary drum filters are used in oil refineries, particularly for filtration of crude oil, but have not found much application in edible fat factories. The differential filtration pressure is limited, and the mucilaginous

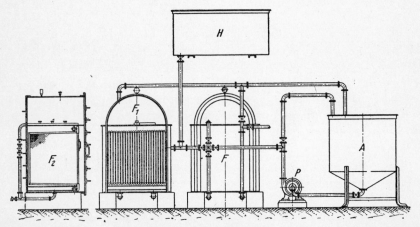

Fig. 21.   Seitz filter plant.

nature of some of the impurities tends to impede the capillary passages of the filter surface, for which reason fairly open-weave cloths are mostly used, and it is frequently necessary to give the oil a second filtration. The advantage of the filter is that the residue is dry and can easily be worked up again with fresh oil seeds, particularly in expeller presses. These continuous filters are not suitable for filtration after bleaching owing to the discontinuous character of that operation.

Fig. 22 (F. p. 18) shows a view of one type of continuous rotary vacuum filter; Fig. 23 a diagram of a section illustrating the principle of operation. The oil is drawn by suction through a cloth stretched over the perforated cylinder and continuously removed from inside. This is divided into separate compartments, which successively can be put under vacuum or pressure by means of an automatically controlled valve system. The pressure blow-back is applied to loosen the filter cake, which is removed from the cylindrical filter surface by a scraper delivering into a conveyor. The whole filter is enclosed in a cover. The method of operation is indicated in Fig. 24. From the tank *A*, provided with stirrer, the turbid oil flows to the rotary filter *B*.

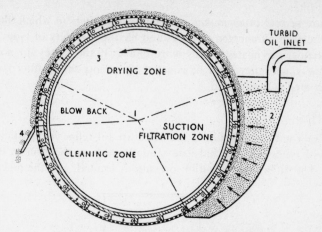

Fig. 23.   Section through rotary vacuum filter.

The residual cake is removed by the scraper *C*. The filtered oil is pumped by the centrifugal pump *F* from the intermediate vacuum container *E*, to which it is drawn from the vacuum section of the filter as the result of the vacuum, provided by pump *D*. If there is a level difference of 11–12 metres between the filter and *E*, the pump *F* can be omitted.

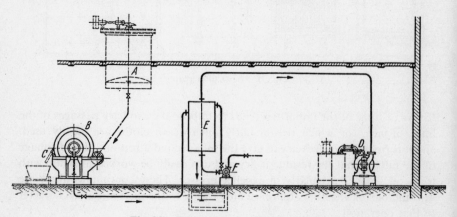

Fig. 24.   Rotary vacuum filtration plant.

General Remarks and Filtration Theory

The filtration process is a separation of liquids from solid particles by means of a porous partition which allows only the liquid to pass through. Pressure is required to overcome the resistance of the partition to penetration by the liquid. The speed of filtration depends on the area of filter surface and on the viscosity of the oil and decreases with increasing viscosity. As the latter decreases with increasing temperature, warm oil is easier to filter than cold. The penetration velocity is at any moment proportional to the propelling force and in inverse ratio to the resistance. The propelling force can be described as the difference in pressure between the front and the back of the filter. The filter cloth or sack is not the true filtering medium, but the cake which is being built up gradually; the average size of the sediment particles is frequently smaller than the pores between the fibres in the cloth, and the real filter medium is the layer of sediment that is retained in and on the surface of the tissue. The building up of this first layer is therefore of decisive importance to obtain satisfactory filtration. The formation of layers changes continuously, and the principles and laws governing flow through capillary passages are difficult to apply, as the passages are not straight, nor uniform or extending through the whole layer. The presence of gummy particles and the gradual compacting of them complicate the conditions. It is therefore doubtful whether a complete mathematical theory can be applied, but on the basis of theoretical and practical considerations the following relations indicate the controlling factors (2) (3) (4).

If R is the resistance in the cake, V the volume of filtrate, and P the differential pressure at time t the following equation is valid:

$$\frac{dV}{dt} = \frac{P}{R}.$$

The resistance can be referred to the resistance of a unit cube. If this specific resistance is r, F the filter surface, measured at right angle to the direction of the flow of the filtrate, and L the thickness of the cake at time t it will be seen that

$$R = \frac{r.L}{F}$$

L is proportional to the amount of solids deposited at time t and proportional to V. If v is the ratio of volume of solids to volume of filtrate, then

$$L = \frac{V.v}{F}$$

and

$$R = \frac{r.V.v}{F^2}$$

If the residue is rigid and homogeneous, r is independent of pressure and velocity, but residues are mostly compressible, crude oil residue to a high degree, bleaching earth residue less. The effect of compressibility is that the specific resistance r increases with increasing pressure. Factor v decreases somewhat with compression, but the total result is an increase in the product $r.v$.

If the initial pressure is too high the first particles will be compressed into a dense mass which chokes the pores of the filter septum, and the filtration velocity falls rapidly. On the other hand, if the initial pressure is low, the first layer remains porous and the speed of filtration is higher. As the cake increases in thickness its resistance becomes greater, and it is necessary to apply higher pumping pressure to obtain the desired speed of percolation. If the filterpress from the beginning operates under full pressure, by means of pump or gravity, the speed of filtration decreases with increasing cake thickness, but if initially a moderate pressure is applied until a good coating of cake is deposited on the cloths, the pressure can gradually be increased during filtration and, when reaching the maximum desirable, maintained constantly at that figure, while the filtration speed slowly falls. This procedure gives the best performance.

BADGER and McCABE, from whose book, *Elements of Chemical Engineering*[2] many of the general remarks about the theory and practice of filtration have

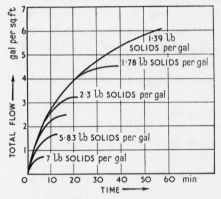

Fig. 25. Filtration curves.

been derived, show graphically the relationship of volume of filtrate and time under constant pressure conditions (Fig. 25). If the total volumes of filtrate, obtained by applying constant pressure from the beginning, are plotted against time, the curves shown in the graph are obtained. Each curve relates to the filtration of a liquid containing per gallon the amount of solid matter shown at each curve, and all filtrations are the same pressure. It will be seen that as the amount of filtrate increases, and thus the thickness of the filter cake, the rate of filtration gradually decreases as shown by the slope of the curves. The break in the curve indicates when the frame in the filterpress is filled.

With compressible residue, as is often the case with crude oils, the rule that the speed of filtration is in direct proportion to the pressure does not always hold good. At low pressures the increment in filtration speed by a small increase in pressure is greater than the reduction in flow resulting from the higher resistance caused by the compression of the layer of residue. If the pressure increases further the two factors cancel out, and at a certain critical pressure maximum filtration speed is achieved. If pressure above the critical is applied the increase in resistance, resulting from compression of the cake, is greater than the effect of the higher pressure, with the result that in spite of the higher pressure, filtration speed is reduced. Residues of this type should therefore be filtered below the critical pressure.

Filtration in filterpresses, particularly in frame presses, leads mostly to a formation of strata. The coarser and heavier particles in the slurry tend to concentrate in the lower parts of the frames, while the finer and lighter particles settle near the top. The resistance to percolation is therefore less in the lower part of the frame.

As stated earlier, centrifugal pumps are particularly suited to meet the conditions of filtration in the oil and fat industry, as they give a non-pulsating flow and their pressure increases as filtration speed diminishes through resistance.

De-stearinization by Filtration

De-stearinization or "Winterizing" are the terms generally applied to the process of removing from the oil certain constituents or impurities which, though soluble at medium and higher temperatures, crystallize out and make the oil turbid or cloudy in cold weather. For instance, a small fraction of solid glycerides, which are natural components of some oils frequently used as salad oils, must be removed as their presence makes the oils cloudy during the winter or when kept in domestic refrigerators. A similar treatment must be given to fish oils, which are used in the manufacture of lacquers, and to certain other oils, for instance, sunflower oil, corn oil, etc., where it is not so much the solid glycerides as a very small proportion of waxes which causes turbidity at low temperature.

The process of winterizing consists in cooling the oil for a protracted period and filtering it in filterpresses or, still better, low pressure filters at temperatures some degrees below that at which the oil is required to remain clear.

The oil is cooled with cold water or brine, or by cooling the air in the storage room. The cooling must be slow enough to enable the higher melting components to form definite well-built crystals. Small crystals which result from too rapid cooling make filtration difficult. Often a suitable filter aid is added to the oil before cooling and the particles act as crystallization centres or nuclei as well as filtration aids. To ensure maintenance of the low temperature during filtration the filters are often placed in the cooling room or the filterpresses are provided with internal channels for cooling.

Fig. 26 shows a diagram of a plant for de-stearinization of sardine oil. *1* is the compressor for the cooling plant, *2* a heat exchanger, *3* brine tank, *4* brine circulation pump, *5* brine coils for cooling the press room, *6* oil cooler, *7* filter pump, *8* filter press, and *9* outlet for the de-stearinized oil.

Winterizing, by the method described has been in use for many years, and for edible purposes has found wide application in U.S.A. for treating cottonseed oil intended for use as salad oil. Newer methods, in which solvents for oils and fats are used to fractionate the glyceride mixtures, as the result of the different solubilities of high and low melting glycerides at various temperatures, have been introduced in recent years, and solvent fractionation of fats and of fatty acid mixtures is now an important industry.

CENTRIFUGAL CLARIFICATION

High-speed centrifugal separators have during the last decades found wide application for a number of purposes in oil treatment plants and refineries. They render excellent service for clarification of oils containing fine suspended

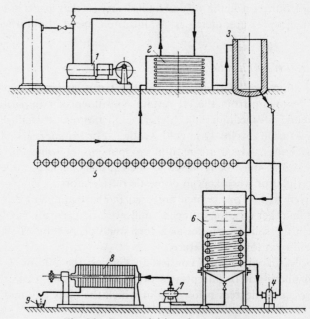

Fig. 26.   De-stearinising plant, diagram.

impurities. The particle size of the impurities and the small difference between their specific gravity and that of the oil make separation by gravity settling a protracted process, whereas the centrifugal force acting on the particles, which in high-speed centrifuges may be several thousand times that of gravity, makes separation practically instantaneous.

For the "clarification" of crude oils, where the impurities are finely suspended solids amounting to a small fraction of 1 per cent, the oil is passed continuously through specially constructed centrifuges, either of the cylindrical rotor type or the bowl and disc type, and the sediment is retained as a peripheral layer on the rotating wall while the clarified oil is discharged in a continuous stream. Where the proportion of impurities is larger and some moisture is also present the treatment is usually called "purification" and the sludge space in the centrifuge is larger. The sludge layer of solids

24

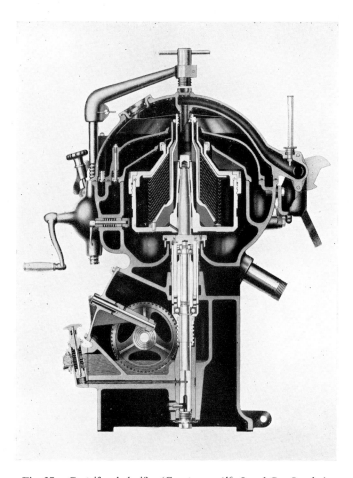

Fig. 27.   Centrifugal clarifier (Courtesy: *Alfa-Laval Co., London*).

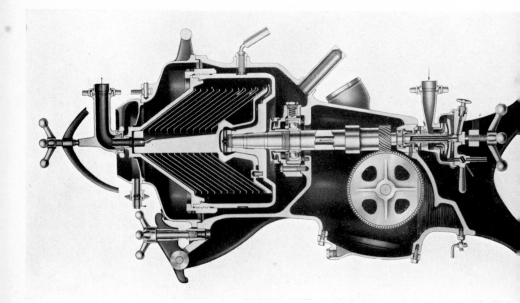

Fig. 29. De Laval centrifuge for continuous discharge of sludge.
(Courtesy: *Alfa-Laval Co., London*).

and water is continuously discharged through an outlet channel from the peripheral layer, while the purified oil, which moves towards the centre of the bowl, is discharged through another outlet. For oils containing relatively large proportions of heavy sludge centrifuges constructed with special sludge-discharging nozzles are used. Fig. 27 shows an Alfa-Laval disc-type centrifuge for purifying palm oil. The crude oil enters through the pipe at the top, and via the central tube reaches the conical distributor at the bottom of the bowl to pass into the separation section. The purified oil flows in the channels between the conical discs towards the centre and out at the top of the bowl neck into the collecting chamber for the discharge pipe, while the watery sludge from the outer layer flows out through the channel between the top cone and the bowl cover.

For many purposes centrifuges with open feed are satisfactory, but if oils have to be protected against the possibility of oxidation by air as, for instance, when clarifying oils containing vitamin A, hermetically sealed separators with bottom feed are used. Fig. 28 shows a centrifuge of this type made by the Alfa-Laval Company. The turbid crude oil is supplied under pressure at the bottom of the hollow central spindle to a small impeller pump which keeps it under pressure during separation. The clarified oil leaves the centrifuge at the top, while the sediment is retained in the bowl. Inlet and outlet ports are connected through pressure-tight glands to the pipes.

Centrifugal clarifiers are used extensively for oils intended for salad and canning oils, for purification of whale and fish oils, for palm oil and other vegetable oils before refining. At various stages in the refining process and in the treatment of by-products centrifugal separators working on the same principle, but of modified design, are also used, and will be described in the appropriate sections.

REFERENCES.

[1] JAMIESON, G. S. and W. E. BAUGHMAN; J. Oil and Fat Ind. 1926 3 75.
[2] BADGER, W. L. and W. L. McCABE; Elements of Chemical Engineering. McGraw-Hill, New York 1936.
[3] WALKER, W. H., LEWIS, W. K., McADAMS, W. H. and E. R. GILLILAND; Principles of Chemical Engineering. McGraw-Hill, New York 1937.
[4] DICKEY, G. D. and C. L. BRYDEN; Theory and Practice of Filtration. Reinhold Publishing Corporation, New York 1946.

3

2

REMOVAL OF FAT-SOLUBLE IMPURITIES

INTRODUCTION

THE preceding chapters have dealt with methods for removing solid fat-insoluble impurities, but even after their removal by settling, filtration or centrifugation fats still contain a number of substances foreign to the glycerides or pure fats. They may be in true solution or in a state of colloidal suspension, and to make fats suitable for edible and many technical purposes all substances which may have an unfavourable effect on flavour, appearance, colour and stability must be eliminated. This is the task of the oil refiners.

These fat-soluble impurities may be proteins, gums, resins, phosphatides, colouring matters, hydrocarbons, ketones, aldehydes and some not yet fully studied, which are largely responsible for the unpleasant taste and odour of crude fats. Some constituents, though not part of the glyceride molecules, are not considered objectionable; they are tasteless, odourless and colourless and stable against heat; these are the sterols and tocopherols, of which the latter are looked upon as desirable ingredients as they have antioxidant properties.

Some of the difficulties of refining are caused by lack of knowledge about the chemical nature of the impurities. For instance comparatively little is known of the composition of some of the gums, resins and some colouring matters in the fats.

Early investigators have found calcium and magnesium salts in mucilages from hot-pressed sunflower oil and in the "break" material from linseed oil. Protein complexes have also been found, but the often contradictory results of analyses of the mucilages and gums are easily explained by the colloidal nature of these compounds. The foreign material accompanying or taken up into the fat depends on the conditions under which the fat is obtained from the seed, such as wetting and heating, crushing, expelling and extracting by solvents, as well as the type of solvent. Furthermore, the mucilage obtained by "break" of the fat at high temperatures, 250–280°C, is no doubt of different composition from that obtained by coagulating the "break" material by hydration (see later). Some fairly recent work by SCHAFRANOWSKAJA[1] included analyses of the mucilage precipitated by hydration from linseed oil, and showed that it consisted of 16 per cent protein, 20 per cent phosphatide, 7·5 per cent carbohydrate and 12·9 per cent mineral matter, whereas mucilage obtained by heat "break" was free from phosphatides.

Colouring matters in fats consist largely of carotenoid pigments, to which are due the yellow and orange tints. Chlorophyll and related pigments are present in some oils, for instance, olive oil and soya bean oil. Brownish tints are often found in crude fats and oils of inferior quality and are probably due to complex decomposition products of carbohydrate and protein; they are difficult to remove by the usual bleaching methods.

Among substances contributing to the development of unpleasant flavours in fats are unsaturated hydrocarbons and degradation products such as ketones (methylheptyl- and methylnonyl-ketones, etc.) and aldehydes, but these are probably only partly responsible for the objectionable taste and odour. The odoriferous compounds in vegetable and animal fats are largely volatile in a current of steam, but some may require to be removed by adsorbents.

All crude fats contain free fatty acids as the result of the action of lipolytic enzymes on the glycerides during storage and treatment of the oil-bearing material ; they are not extraneous impurities, being part of the glyceride molecule, and fats may contain 0·2–0·3 per cent or more free fatty acids without the taste or odour being noticeably affected, unless the fatty acids are of low or medium molecular value (myristic, lauric and lower molecular value acids). High-molecular saturated fatty acids, even when present to the extent of 15 per cent can hardly be detected organoleptically; unsaturated fatty acids, however, affect the taste.

High acidity in crude fat is nevertheless a warning that it has been obtained from inferior raw materials stored unsuitably or too long, or wrongly processed; such fats contain often in addition to the free fatty acids excessive amounts of mucilage and other foreign matters, compared with fats with low free fatty acid content. Purification becomes more difficult the higher the free fatty acid percentage; consequently crude fats are frequently evaluated according to their acidity, generally calculated as percentage oleic acid, although with coconut and palm kernel oils the calculation is now as a rule based on lauric acid. The elimination of the free fatty acids by neutralization with caustic soda is the most effective method of cleaning the crude fats, as with the soap formed by the neutralization of the free acids a large proportion of the other impurities are also removed.

During the last fifty years certain standard methods of refining have gained general acceptance and widespread application, and only in quite recent years have other and special methods been developed. In most refineries the following operations are carried out:

1. De-gumming or de-sliming.
2. De-acidifying, mostly by neutralization.
3. De-colouring or bleaching.
4. De-odorizing.

Operations 1 and 2 are often combined in the so-called lye-refining method. It is frequently contended that it is an advantage to carry out operation 1 first, as the presence of mucilage during neutralization increases losses through formation of emulsions and lowers quality. Many refiners state, however, that if proper attention is given to temperatures, concentration of lye, speed of stirring and type of neutralizing chemical, loss from the combined operations and cost of processing is less than from the two separate operations.

I. Pre-treatment by De-gumming

A number of methods exist for removing gums, resins, proteins and phosphatides from crude fats. The best known is the treatment of the crude fat with dilute alkali, whereby at the same time the free fatty acids are converted into soaps which, when separating from the fat, absorb gums, etc., as well as some of the colouring matters, and thus effect a thorough purification. By neutralizing in this manner fat which contains mucilage emulsions may be formed which reduce the yield of neutral fat, because the soap solution and the mucilage by their strong emulsifying power may entangle and tenaciously retain larger proportions of neutral fat than if the crude fat had first been de-gummed. The quality of the recoverable acid oil from the soap will also be reduced through the content of impurities.

De-gumming by Means of Acid

One of the oldest and most effective methods for separation and removal of mucilage is the treatment of the crude fats with small quantities of strong sulphuric acid at low or moderate temperatures, but care and experience in the technique is required to obtain successful results. The method is used mostly on gummy oils for certain technical purposes, for instance, for acid refining of rape oil for burning oils or sanctuary oils, where mucilage would cause choking and charring of the wick, and for pre-treatment of fats before splitting. Fish and whale oils, difficult to hydrogenate, are also frequently treated with acid before hydrogenation. In the edible fat industry pre-treatment with sulphuric acid alone is very rarely used; it is, however, sometimes used in conjunction with fuller's earth.

Sulphuric acid has the effect of precipitating and charring the proteins, gums, colouring pigments, etc. Such a highly reactive material can, however, attack the glycerides themselves and cause slight sulphonation, which is to be avoided, as it often produces a red colour in the fat which cannot be removed again. The concentration of the acid must therefore not be too high, and the temperature during the treatment should generally not exceed 25–30°C. Intensive stirring of the mixture is important to avoid localized excessive reaction. Usually acid of 66°Bé is used as higher concentration entails risk to the fat.

The following examples describe how rape oil is refined with sulphuric acid to obtain a good lamp burning oil:

To crude rape oil in a tank with conical bottom, sometimes lead-lined against corrosion, sulphuric acid of 66°Bé is added in a thin stream or as a fine spray. The proportion of acid depends on the quality of the oil and is largely a matter of experience, but is generally 0·5–1·5 per cent. The rate of addition is such that the temperature does not increase beyond 30°C. When the right amount of acid has been added the colour of the oil changes to a greenish tint through the formation of fine dark green flakes, which gradually darken to a blackish flocculent precipitate. Examination of a sample of the oil in transmitted light or on a white porcelain plate shows charred mucilage floating in the clear yellowish oil. The easy separation and settling of the precipitate indicates the success of the operation and that the right quantity of acid has been used. Immediately after the flocculation 1–2 per cent hot water is added to dilute the acid and prevent reaction of any excess with the oil. After settling of the residue and aqueous acid-layer on the bottom of the tank these are run off, and the treated oil is washed thoroughly in a suitable tank of acid-resisting material with hot water until free from mineral acid.

In another modification of the process 1·5 per cent of acid of 66°Bé is sprayed on the surface of the oil, which is left till the green flakes are formed, when 1·5 per cent milk of lime is added to prevent any sulphonation effect on the oil. This is then heated under gradually increasing vacuum to about 80°C, and 1·5 per cent activated bleaching earth is drawn into the vessel, when all water has been removed by evaporation. The oil is now heated to about 100°C and filtered through paper and cloth. The purity of the oil is ascertained by a burning test, when it should burn with a steady flame and leave no ash.

A sulphuric acid pre-treatment is also frequently given to fats before they are split by the autoclave treatment or by the Twitchell reagent, and to acid oils intended for fatty acid distillation.

Linseed oil is often acid-treated to remove the bodies causing the "break". There are a number of variations of the process, but in principle it can be described as follows:

1–1·5 per cent sulphuric acid of 60°Bé (about 80 per cent strength) is added to the cold crude oil and the mixture stirred for about 1 hour. After settling the supernatant oil is drawn off by means of a swivel pipe to a washing tank and heated with direct steam to about 100°C, settled again and the acid water run off. The oil is dried and about 0·5 per cent activated earth is added and stirred into the oil at 60–65°C. After filtration the clarified oil will be found to be bleached to some extent, but as a rule the free fatty acid percentage will have increased slightly.

One of the few cases where a sulphuric acid pre-treatment is given to oil intended for edible purposes is when crude rape oil is treated for removal of mineral matter. It is sometimes found that crude rape oil contains 200–300 p.p.m. of mineral matter, principally iron, lime and alumina compounds which, if left in the oil, may cause difficulties in subsequent refining operations. They are nearly completely removed by a pre-treatment at 100°C with about 10 per cent of a 2 per cent solution of sulphuric acid, the mixture being agitated by passing direct steam through until frothing ceases; settling and separation follows.

De-gumming with other acids is used in some refineries, particularly when treating groundnut oil. An effective method is the use of about 0·4 per cent of a twice-normal hydrochloric acid, added to the oil at 20–25°C. After good mixing 0·5–1 per cent fibrous meal of groundnut husks is added to aid filtration. Removal of the impurities or "foots" by draining is sometimes preferred to avoid absorption of nutty flavour from the husk meal.

I. G. Farbenindustrie A.G. has patented[2] a method in which 1–4 per cent concentrated hydrochloric acid is added to dry oil at 80°C in course of 10–20 min. while stirring vigorously. During continued but slow stirring the mucilage forms lumps and sinks to the bottom of the vessel.

Metallgesellschaft A.G. has patented[3] a de-gumming method employing a mixture of calcium chloride and hydrochloric acid. The oil at 50°C is stirred for a short time with 4 per cent strong hydrochloric acid and 3 per cent of a 30 per cent calcium chloride solution.

In a Russian process proposed by BAUMAN and GRABOWSKI[4], for de-gumming sunflower oil, this is first treated with a 0·5 per cent sulphuric acid solution followed by a sodium chloride solution of 5°Bé. After removal by draining of the aqueous layer the oil is kept cold for about 24 hours. The settled oil is easy to filter, and it is claimed that in subsequent refining there is a saving of 35–40 per cent caustic lye. This method can also be applied to linseed oil.

In other acid de-gumming methods phosphoric acid and its salts are used. According to an *I. G. Farbenindustrie A.G.* patent[5] phosphatides and mucilage are removed from soya bean oil by means of phosphoric acid of 40–65 per cent strength. The oil at 35°C is stirred with 1 per cent phosphoric acid, quickly heated to 60°C and, after the addition of 0·2 per cent water and 10 min. stirring, left to settle. After draining off the slimy layer any phosphoric acid left in the oil is neutralized with ammonia, which causes precipitation of any residual mucilage.

A similar process has been patented by *Harburger Oelwerke*, BRINKMAN and MERGELL[6]. Oil is treated with 0·1–0·8 per cent phosphoric acid (sp. gr. 1·55) at 70°C, kieselguhr and cellulose used as filter aids and lime for neutralizing the acid. De-gumming with phosphoric acid has also been proposed by the *Sherwin Williams Co.*[7]

A better effect than with free phosphoric acid is claimed with the alkali phosphates. *I. G. Farbenindustrie A.G.*[8] have patented the use of trisodium phosphate, sodium pyrophosphate, etc. This patent also proposes the use for de-gumming of aqueous solutions of sulphurous acid, soda, salt, sodium bisulphite and other salts. An American patent by the *Alexander Wacker Co. for Electrochemical Industry*[9] also states that pyrophosphates are effective for de-gumming.

In the methods mentioned the process has been carried out at relatively low temperatures with dilute solutions of the various chemicals. Patents claiming the use of anhydrous boric acid or its esters at considerably higher temperatures have been taken out by *I. G. Farbenindustrie A.G.*[10]. Cottonseed oil, for instance, is heated in vacuum with 1 per cent anhydrous boric acid to 130°C. This treatment is stated to reduce subsequent refining loss by 45 per cent. In place of boric acid its esters with polyhydric alcohols (glycerol, etc.) can be used.

THURMAN reported already in 1923[11] that boric acid could precipitate proteins, phosphatides and other impurities from crude cottonseed oil.

β-Naphthalinsulphonic acid has also de-gumming effect at temperatures of 70–200°C. Sesamé oil, for instance, may be treated with 0·8 per cent of this acid for 5–15 min. at 160°C.

In all acid pre-treatments, and in all pretreatments with corrosive chemicals, it is important to consider the suitability of the material of the plant for the particular ingredients and the conditions under which they are used. If, for example, oil-soluble iron salts are formed by the acid attacking the reaction vessel, the stability and colour of the oil may suffer.

De-gumming by Heat

The fats which can be de-gummed by acid treatment respond generally also to de-gumming by heating to 240–280°C, as the heat causes coagulation of the colloidal mucilage and produces a "break". The precipitate is, however, difficult to filter, and a loss of fatty matter occurs in the filter residue. Some oils also undergo changes by polymerization and thickening, and the method is therefore rarely used except in connection with treatment for purposes other than de-gumming.

De-gumming by Hydration

Phosphatides, proteins and some other colloidal impurities, which are either dissolved in the oil or in very fine colloidal dispersion as long as they are anhydrous and the oil is dry, swell when wetted or hydrated and form gels of higher specific gravity, separate from the oil in flocculent particles and, if the oil is left quiescent, gradually sink to the bottom of the vessel.

Crude oils from the solvent extraction process have often undergone a hydration treatment, if steam has been blown through the oil to remove the last few per cent of the solvent, or if the crude oil has been specially treated to recover "lecithin", the mixed phosphatide present in soya bean oil to the extent of 1·5-3 per cent, and in at times economically recoverable— but smaller proportions, in other oils such as groundnut and rape oil. Most crude oils contain, however, a sufficient amount of hydratable impurities to justify a hydration treatment before de-acidification. All these are in principle similar and consist in injecting a small proportion, 2–5 per cent, of warm or hot water, stirring vigorously and finally separating the hydrated colloids from the purified oil. A few examples will indicate some typical variations in details.

The simplest method is to warm the oil to about 80°C and then blow

31

direct steam in from a perforated coil, gradually warming the oil to 100°C, continue the "boiling" for 10–15 min. and then leave the residue or "foots" to settle. The amount of steam condensed should be 3–5 per cent, which will allow the "foots" to be removed by draining. Some refiners prefer, after steaming is finished, to spray a weak solution of salt, or sprinkle about 2 per cent common salt, on the surface. This helps to flocculate and settle the impurities, which often carry with them some of the colouring matter. The use of salt or a salt solution is very common in clarification of animal fats and fairly frequent on vegetable oils and fats.

Another method employs intimate mixing of oil with 2–5 per cent hot water at about 95°C, the best proportion to be determined by preliminary experiment, as it depends on the type and origin of the oil. It is rather important to have the correct proportion of water, and failure of this apparently simple process occurs occasionally, as too little water gives insufficient hydration, and thus incomplete removal of colloids, and too much water may lead to emulsification troubles with consequent loss of oil. Settling or centrifugal separation follows.

If one of the objects is to recover from the crude oil the phosphatides as a valuable by-product, some manufacturers find it advantageous to commence the hydration treatment at a low temperature, 25–35°C, and gradually raise the temperature to about 85°C by means of direct steam, by which time the percentage of moisture in the oil should be about 4 and the mixture ready for centrifugation.

It is held by some operators that the use of direct steam makes it difficult to control the moisture content of the mixture, and as it is important that the recovered phosphatides do not contain excessive water, but just sufficient to flow easily from the centrifuges, hot water is used in controlled amounts. The crude oil is heated to about 50°C, and under thorough stirring hot water to the extent of 2–4 per cent is sprayed on to the surface. The lower temperatures in this process assist separation and hydration, and in course of 15–30 min., during which period flocculation occurs and agitation is kept at a slower but sufficient speed to keep the hydrated colloids evenly distributed, the mixture is ready for separation by centrifuge.

The leading makers of centrifugal separators build special types for de-gumming and phosphatide removal after hydration; the separator bowl is adapted for continuous discharge of the thick sludge deposited at the periphery, while the clear oil is delivered from another outlet (Fig. 29, facing p. 25).

In an American patent[12] AYRES and CLARK explain their views on the hydration process for removal of colloids and its economic importance in connection with alkali neutralization of the free fatty acids, and they emphasize the importance of the correct amount of water for successful hydration. They recommend also the use of an aqueous solution containing a little starch, salt and alkali; the starch is suggested because its hydrophilic properties lessen the possibility of a water-in-oil emulsion being formed;

32

the quantity added is 0·2 per cent of a 2 per cent starch solution, and the temperature should be about 60°C, while the mixture is being vigorously stirred.

Other American patents by KELLEY[13], TURNER[14] and BAYLIS[15] describe similar hydration processes.

The use of very dilute alkali solutions have been recommended by various people as a pre-treatment to alkali neutralization proper. NJEMIROWSKI[16] describes the use of a dilute NaOH solution of 0·001–0·002 per cent strength at 30–50°C. CLAYTON[17] uses also dilute alkali, but under pressure and at a temperature of 42°C, followed by sudden pressure release.

The removal of mucilage and phosphatides is of special importance in connection with hydrogenation of oils. The nickel catalyst used for hydrogenation contains always some phosphorus, as even thoroughly cleaned oils contain traces of phosphatides[18]. These can be entirely eliminated when the oil is treated with a large excess of lye of 1–2 per cent strength, to which has been added 10–15 per cent sodium chloride. It is claimed that after prolonged action of the lye, the phosphatides are hydrolized and the liberated phosphoric acid dissolved in the lye, while soap is salted out and forms an intermediate layer between the purified oil and the lye.

For the practical application of the de-acidification method for fats by distillation with steam *I. G. Farbenindustrie A.G.* has proposed a de-gumming by hydration technique[19] which ensures the removal of mucilage by dispersing in the oil a small quantity of water at 60°C or more and then cooling the mixture to room temperature in less than 30 min. This method can, for instance, be used for recovery of lecithin from solvent extracted soya bean oil. With oils heavily contaminated with mucilage slightly acidified water can be used. For example, crude soya bean oil is mixed with 1 per cent acid water at 70–75°C in a turbo-mixer until a colloidal dispersion is formed, which during subsequent cooling separates as flocculent flakes. A continuous cooler reduces the temperature to 20°C and to the cold oil is added 0·05 per cent soda ash while stirring. The precipitate is stated to contain only about 10 per cent oil.

A similar process for de-gumming is described in another patent by *I. G. Farbenindustrie A.G.*[20].

De-gumming is a common pre-treatment of crude oils in connection with the continuous neutralization process with alkalis. The oil, after continuous filtration to remove insoluble impurities, is pumped through a heater to a mixer, where a small quantity of hot water or steam is injected, and then to a closed tank, where the flow of oil is slowed down sufficiently to enable hydration and flocculation to take place. From the outlet of the tank the mixture passes continuously to a specially constructed centrifuge, where separation of clear oil and sludge is effected. This process will be further referred to later under continuous refining methods.

The use of salt or salt solutions in combination with other ingredients has already been mentioned. Salt solution alone is also used; for instance, crude groundnut oil can be de-gummed by heating the oil to 96–98°C and stirring into it 5 per cent of a sodium chloride solution of 3 per cent strength, added in portions of 0·5–1 per cent to allow frothing, which often occurs with this oil, to subside before the next addition. After settling, generally about 1 hour, the brine layer and sediment is drawn off and the oil washed by spraying on it 15–20 per cent hot water. This is then settled and drawn off. The loss of oil with the residue is small, generally less than 0·2 per cent. Some refiners add the oil to the brine solution and boil through with direct steam for mixing; in that case frothing must be carefully watched.

De-gumming with Adsorbents

De-gumming with various adsorbents is a very common practice. A number of inorganic adsorbents, such as kieselguhr, charcoal, fuller's earth, activated clays and many proprietary products have coagulating and adsorbing properties towards the colloidal impurities and colouring matters in oils. Their use for bleaching will be dealt with later. Where they are used principally for clarification and de-gumming 0·5–1 per cent suffices as a rule, unless the oil is very rich in mucilage, when higher proportions are required. An excessive amount is undesirable, as some oil is always absorbed in the adsorbent and only partly recoverable and then of a lower quality. Less than 0·5 per cent of adsorbent, calculated on the quantity of oil, is hardly effective. When the adsorbent is an activated earth or carbon there is usually a distinct bleaching effect, and if the activated earth is of the strongly acid type the effect is similar to the earlier described de-gumming by acid followed by earth. There is, as a rule, a slight increase in the free fatty acid content of the oil when acid earth is used, the increase being proportional to the temperature employed. The method of de-gumming with adsorbents is not so effective, if it is a question of removing phosphatides, but in oils, where the content of these is low, adsorbent treatment is very useful, as it helps to obtain higher yields in neutralization with alkali and, through the preliminary bleaching effect, lessens the final bleaching cost.

The use of adsorbents for clarification is a very old process, although patents for new modifications are frequently taken out. The adsorbent must be finely dispersed in the oil, and subsequent filtration must be at moderate pressure. The temperature of the treatment varies with circumstances and is generally between 60° and 100°C. At the higher temperatures, and particularly if the oil is intended for edible purposes, it is advisable to work the process under vacuum. As a method of purifying oil for hydrogenation the adsorbent treatment is very effective.

Physical Methods of De-gumming

From time to time patents have been granted for de-gumming oils by causing flocculation and precipitation of mucilage and finely suspended particles as the result of electric discharges through the oil. LEIMDÖRFER[21] claims, that when oils at 100°C pass through a high tension electrical field, flocculation of mucilage takes place. The practical application of such a process is, however, doubtful, as are the various processes for ultrafiltration, which have been suggested in the literature.

De-gumming with Special Reagents

Many chemicals have been recommended in the patent literature as effective de-gumming agents. *I. G. Farbenindustrie A.G.* in an earlier mentioned patent[20] has included treatment with reagents which are immiscible with oil and without chemical action towards the impurities. In addition to salt and aqueous salt solutions, as already described, such anhydrous chemicals as formic amide, glycerol, glacial acetic acid, formic acid, glycol and other alcohols have been proposed.

Other reagents, for which similar effect is claimed, are citric and oxalic acids and their sodium salts, zinc chloride, sodium oleate, calcium sulphate and others, but little has been heard about their use in industry.

Alum, tannin and tannic acid salts were at one time widely used in practice for clarification, and although they have largely been replaced by simpler and equally efficient methods, many refiners still find a de-gumming treatment with tannic acid particularly effective on certain qualities of crude oil, such as soya bean oil or groundnut oil. In such cases the crude oil is heated to about 100°C and a solution containing 0·04 per cent tannic acid and 0·46 per cent salt in 10 per cent water, calculated on the amount of oil, is added under brisk stirring for about 15 min. Agitation is then stopped, about 20 per cent hot water sprayed on the surface of the oil, and after settling the sludge is drained off. Washing with smaller amounts of hot water is repeated to remove traces of the reagents if necessary.

Oils containing sulphur, whether derived from sulphur contained in the solvent used for their extraction or from sulphur-containing tissues, should be treated for removal of the sulphur compounds, particularly if intended for hydrogenation. As a rule this is effected by the alkali neutralization process and adsorption. A special de-sulphuring treatment with compounds of copper, nickel or lead has been patented by *I. G. Farbenindustrie A.G.*[22]. As example is mentioned the use of 3 per cent of a 10 per cent nickel sulphate solution and 3 per cent of a 10 per cent soda solution at 60–90°C.

De-gumming with Alkali

The most important and in industry most frequently applied method of de-gumming is the refining and neutralization process with a caustic soda solution. The soap solution, formed by the neutralization of the free fatty acids, carries with it, when settling, most of the impurities and, when an appropriate concentration of caustic is used, a proportion of the colouring matter. The treatment with caustic soda is not only one of the oldest, but also still the most frequently used method of refining and de-acidification of fats and oils for edible use. It will be dealt with in detail in that section.

The method is, however, also frequently used for oils intended for technical purposes, particularly when a reduction in the free fatty acid content of the oil is desirable or necessary. Linseed oil, for instance, is often alkali-treated to make it more suitable for the manufacture of stand oils, varnish and paints. The methods vary in details, but in principle they all provide for the addition of a caustic soda solution in excess of that required for neutralization or in the amount needed to reduce the free fatty acid percentage to the desired level. De-gumming and acidity reduction are thus combined. Temperatures of operation and concentration of caustic differ from place to place, but are usually 50°–90°C and 6–12 per cent strength of caustic. The technique is similar to that of neutralizing oils for edible use (see p. 38).

Combined de-gumming and neutralization with a caustic soda solution is nearly always applied to oils intended for hydrogenation, as the presence of colloidal impurities reduces the activity of the catalyst, and free fatty acids combine with the nickel in the catalyst, forming nickel soaps which also lessen the activity, dissolve in the oil and cause discoloration. The pre-treatment of oils for hydrogenation is similar to the alkali neutralization treatment for edible oils.

General Remarks about Pre-treatment

Although some of the many methods described for pre-treatment of fats and oils prior to de-acidification may have special application on some raw materials in certain circumstances, by far the most important are filtration and centrifugal separation for removal of insoluble impurities, and hydration and adsorption treatment followed by centrifugal and filtration separation respectively, as well as alkali treatment for removal of colloidally dispersed or dissolved substances. The latter treatments will, however, also deal effectively with the solid impurities, and it is a question of economics whether it pays to have two separate steps or to combine them in one process.

The case for pre-treatment is generally stated as follows:

1. Removal of impurities improves the stability of the oil; purified oils show a slower increase in acidity during storage than untreated oils.

2. Good de-gumming will in many cases be a sufficient treatment for oils for technical purposes, for instance, linseed oil for lacquers.

3. It facilitates the further refining processes and reduces the refining losses, particularly when de-acidification with caustic soda is used.

There is among refiners a difference of opinion as regards point 3, as many maintain that the combined losses from pre-treatment and alkali neutralization exceed those from alkali neutralization of non-pre-treated oil, where appropriate methods for dealing with the impurities in the latter have been applied. Furthermore, the cost of special equipment for pre-treatment is not out-weighed by any saving in oil. On the other hand, neutralization by-products from pre-cleaned oils and fats are cleaner and of higher value than those containing the impurities from the neutralization of non-pre-treated crude oils, and a balance sheet should be drawn up in every case to ascertain the pros and cons.

In the modern continuous neutralization processes where the possibility of variation in technique is less flexible than in the older batch processes, pre-treatment by de-gumming seems to have been well established.

II. Neutralization or De-acidification

The term neutralization is generally applied to the process of removing the free fatty acids from crude fats and oils, and for many years the only method used industrially was neutralization with bases such as caustic soda or lime. As the refinery industry developed, particularly in connection with the preparation of fats for edible purposes, other methods were evolved, such as removal of free fatty acids by distillation, by solvent extraction, or by combination of these with neutralization methods. Re-combination by esterification of the free fatty acids, formed by hydrolysis of the crude fat, with fresh glycerol, thus re-forming glycerides to replace those split by hydrolysis, has also in some places been developed on industrial scale. It would therefore be more correct at present to describe the process as de-acidification of fats. This section deals with the various methods used industrially for elimination of free fatty acids.

The principal methods of de-acidification used in industry at present are:

A. Neutralization with caustic alkali.
    (a) Batch process with strong caustic.
    (b) Batch process with weak caustic.
    (c) Batch process with mixed concentrations.
    (d) Plant for batch processes.
    (e) Continuous processes.
    (f) Soapstock.
B. Neutralization with alkali carbonate.
C. Neutralization with lime and other chemicals.
D. De-acidification by distillation.
E. De-acidification by solvent extraction.
F. De-acidification by esterification.

Of these methods, those under A are the most important and most widely applied. In recent years those under B have made much progress, particularly in continuous processes, although as an after-treatment one of the A methods is often applied. Methods under C are only used in special cases on limited scale. De-acidification methods under D and F are as a rule only used on fats of high acidity and, in the case of F, when glycerine is cheap. Both methods require usually an after-treatment by one of the A methods. The industrial scale application of the E method is a very recent introduction, and its development is largely dependent on cost and availability of the solvents.

NEUTRALIZATION OF FATS WITH CAUSTIC ALKALI

Both from the point of view of cost and of efficiency the only caustic alkali used industrially is caustic soda. It has already been mentioned that a caustic soda solution has the combined effect of purifying, de-gumming, neutralizing and part-decolouring. It combines with the free fatty acids to form sodium soaps, which help to remove impurities and some of the colour, but these soaps also have a tendency to form emulsions, in which some of the neutralized fat is dispersed, thus passing into the less valuable by-products. In certain circumstances the alkali may also attack some of the neutral fat, and if used in excess—and a certain excess is nearly always used—may cause the formation of a larger amount of soap than justified by the free fatty acid content. It is the skill of the refiner to ensure, by the adoption of appropriate methods, that these two sources of loss, namely through emulsions and over-saponification, are minimized as far as possible, without interfering with the achievement of good results as far as quality is concerned.

While in Europe the edible fats industry in its early days relied for raw materials on animal fats and cold-pressed vegetable oils, which needed none or very mild refining, the growth in America of the cottonseed milling industry necessitated the development of methods for converting the blackish-brown crude oil into a cleaner light-coloured oil, more suitable for technical and edible purposes. The caustic soda treatment was found very efficient for that purpose and was therefore developed early in U.S.A. In the crude cottonseed oil from undecorticated seeds is present a relatively high proportion of impurities, phosphatides, mucilage, protein, gossypol, dark pigments, etc., which must be removed, as well as the free fatty acids. Even oil from decorticated seeds needs a rather drastic treatment with caustic soda. To get a sufficiently purified oil an excess of caustic soda beyond that required for neutralization of the free fatty acids is essential, and over-saponification takes place; therefore, to obtain a bright oil, loss of some neutral oil cannot be avoided. As different consignments of crude cottonseed oil, even if similar in free fatty acid content, vary considerably in their response to the caustic soda purification treatment, it is advisable to make preliminary laboratory tests to ascertain the excess of caustic which will ensure good results.

THURMAN[23] has found that the non-fatty impurities which have to be removed, amount on an average to 0·9–1 per cent in cottonseed oil, 0·2–0·4 per cent in groundnut oil, 0·1–0·2 per cent in coconut oil and 0·5 per cent in soya bean oil. If, for instance, a crude oil contains 2 per cent free fatty acids (f.f.a.), 1 per cent impurities and 0·25 per cent moisture, the theoretical yield from neutralizing or refining would be 96·75 per cent, but, as stated, this is not attainable in practice. The aim of the refiner is to approach it as nearly as possible without jeopardizing quality.

The quantitative efficiency of neutralization is expressed in different ways. Some refiners express it as the "refining factor", which is the total loss from the neutralization treatment, including washing, divided by the free fatty acid percentage of the crude oil, as ascertained by titration. If, for instance, an oil with 3 per cent f.f.a. gives a yield of 94 per cent, i.e., 6 per cent loss, the factor is $\dfrac{6}{3} = 2$. The same oil, if purified and de-gummed before neutralization, involving a loss of 0·3 per cent may show a f.f.a. percentage of 2·9 per cent and a neutralizing loss of 5·22 per cent, in which case the factor is $\dfrac{5·22}{2·9} = 1·8$, but to this should be added the loss of oil in the pre-treatment, which may amount to 0·15 per cent, in which case the total loss is 5·37 per cent. The combined factor is therefore $\dfrac{5·37}{2·9} = 1·85$. In addition to the gain in yield there is also an improvement of the quality of the by-product from neutralization, soapstock, by the previous removal of the impurities.

Other refiners ascertain the total fatty matter recoverable from soapstock and wash waters, and the percentage of that, calculated on the crude oil, divided by the f.f.a. percentage of the crude oil is called the "fatty acid factor". If loss of fat in the by-product recovery process is high, this method will give an unduly favourable factor and will cause a high "unaccounted for" loss in the process balance-sheet. In well-controlled refineries, and where weighing of the neutralized oil is inconvenient, it is, however, an easy and practical control on refinery efficiency.

Another method of checking refining efficiency consists in determining in the crude oil the actual percentage of neutral glycerides and the yield of neutral oil from the process, calculated as the percentage of weight of the crude oil. If, for instance, the former is 97 per cent of the crude oil and the yield of neutral oil is 95 per cent, the efficiency is said to be $\dfrac{95}{97} \times 100 = 98$ per cent.

The "Wesson" method which is in general use in U.S.A.[24] is based on a standardized test, indicating the total loss of fatty acids and impurities which would under the most favourable conditions be incurred by the refining with caustic soda. This "Wesson loss", the minimum attainable, is then compared with the actual result in factory operations and the efficiency based on the comparison.

The neutralization process is preceded by a titration test with deci-normal alkali for the free fatty acid content. In most oils and fats the percentage of f.f.a. is calculated on the assumption that their molecular weight is that of oleic acid, namely 282. For some fats this figure is too high, in view of the average molecular weight of the acids, and therefore for these fats lower figures are generally used, for instance, for coconut oil 206, for palm kernel oil 220, and for palm oil 256. Based on this test the refiner calculates the amount of neutralization liquid he requires and decides the excess necessary as well as the strength of the solution. There is no uniform method of expressing strength; degrees Baumé (°Bé), degrees Twaddel (°Tw), specific gravity (sp. gr.), percentage strength (%) and normality (N) are all used according to the preference of the refiner. The following Table I gives a comparison of these expressions for caustic soda solutions, which is the almost universally used neutralizing agent.

TABLE I

°Bé	Sp. gr.	°Tw	% NaOH in sol.	Approx. Normality
2	1·014	2·8	1·2	0·3
4	1·029	5·8	2·5	0·62
6	1·045	9·0	3·79	0·95
8	1·060	12·0	5·2	1·3
10	1·075	15·0	6·58	1·65
12	1·091	18·2	8·07	2·0
14	1·108	21·6	9·5	2·37
16	1·125	25·0	11·06	2·76
18	1·142	28·4	12·69	3·17
20	1·162	32·4	14·35	3·6
22	1·180	36·0	16·0	4·0
24	1·200	40·0	17·81	4·45
26	1·220	44·0	19·65	4·9
28	1·241	48·2	21·55	5·39
30	1·263	52·6	23·50	5·88
32	1·285	57	25·50	6·4

Neutralization with Strong Caustic alkali

While in Europe neutralization is generally done with weak caustic solutions, the strong caustic soda method has been almost universal in America, where crude cottonseed oil for many years was the most common oil for refining, and for this oil the strong caustic method is particularly effective. It not only neutralizes the oil, but thoroughly purifies it and generally achieves a partial bleaching, thereby facilitating the secondary bleaching operation.

This is of considerable importance in America, where most of the refined cottonseed oil is used for the manufacture of colourless shortenings, while in Europe most of the highly refined oils and fats are used in yellow coloured margarines. It is therefore not surprising that the "strong caustic" refining technique has been particularly highly developed in U.S.A. The term "strong caustic" is not very definite, but generally lyes of 10°Bé (6·6 per cent strength) or more are meant.

The choice of concentration is often based on standardized preliminary laboratory tests—in U.S.A. on the official methods of the American Oil Chemists' Society[25]—which indicate the strength of lye and the excess required to give appropriate results, and are also frequently used for commercial evaluation of the crude oil. Experience also plays a part in selecting the concentration of alkali. A further point influencing selection is the concentration of fatty matter desired in the by-product soapstock. Where this has to be sent to a soap factory for use in soap-making, it is obviously an advantage that it contains as high a proportion of fatty matter as possible, consistent with ease of handling.

The following points must therefore be taken into consideration in making a choice of lye concentration:

1. Nature of the soapstock: A strong solution of caustic soda produces, even at a relatively high water content, a very viscous soapstock, which when cold may set into a solid mass. A concentration of solution should therefore be chosen that will still allow the soapstock to flow out of the neutralizing vessel at 60–70°C. Fats with low iodine value yield a very firm soapstock, but even liquid oils, such as cottonseed oil, form with strong caustic solutions a very thick and tough soapstock. The use of too strong a concentration of caustic in excess may cause salting out of the soap from the soapstock, which should be avoided.
2. The amount of neutral oil saponified: The higher the concentration of the caustic solution, the greater the risk of some neutral oil being attacked and forming soap in addition to that formed from the free fatty acids. This means higher refining loss.
3. The amount of neutral oil occluded in the soapstock: The more dilute the caustic solution the greater the tendency of the soap solution to form emulsions with some of the neutral oil. Generally, fats with lower free fatty acid content can be satisfactorily refined with relatively weak lyes, whereas high-acid fats require stronger lyes. Against the lesser danger of over-saponification with weak lyes must be set the increased loss of neutral oil through emulsification.
4. The rate of separation of neutral oil and soapstock: The temperature of processing and the concentration of lye should be so chosen that the soapstock, when it "breaks" in fine flakes in the oil, settles rapidly and compactly on the bottom of the vessel. Slow spongy settling generally means bad separation and loss of neutralized oil by occlusion.

5. De-coloration of neutralized oil: The weaker the lye the greater the excess of caustic required to obtain, also in addition to the neutralization, a good bleaching effect in the oil.

6. The acidity of the crude fat: As mentioned under 3, the strength of the lye depends often on the acidity of the crude material; the higher the free fatty acid percentage, the stronger the lye. A definite relationship between acidity and concentration of lye cannot, however, be laid down, as it varies from fat to fat and depends on its previous history, the content of fat-soluble surface-active substances, oxidation products, etc. While therefore the general rule is a guide, it is better to ascertain the most favourable conditions for refining by preliminary tests. The concentration of lye, when working with strong caustic, varies in practice from 10°Bé–24°Bé, but all the above-mentioned points must be taken into consideration.

Some examples of methods employed in neutralizing with strong lye will be given below, but in all methods certain principles have to be observed.

When soap particles are formed, i.e., when the "break" occurs, the temperature should be high enough to permit the soap to separate and settle quickly. This can be tested on a small sample which should show soap particles floating in the clear oil and settling easily in the test glass, indicating that the stirring of the mass can be stopped and the oil left for settling.

Caustic soda is apt to absorb carbon dioxide from the air, or may contain carbonate as an impurity. If excessive amounts are present carbon dioxide may be evolved at the temperature of neutralization and cause a scum of soap particles to be formed on the surface. This must be avoided.

A scum can also be caused by too high a neutralization temperature, particularly if air is occluded in the crude oil; its release by high temperature may lead to an aerated soap scum floating to the surface. Many refiners prefer, where the plant is suitable, to de-aerate the oil before neutralization.

Stirring should be rapid enough for intimate mixing of lye and oil, but there must be no tendency to centrifugal separation of soap at the walls of the vessel. To obtain a uniform compact settling of the soapstock there must be no severe eddying, and two-speed stirrers are an advantage, so that after the lye has been added and well mixed in, stirring until "break" takes place can be at slower speed. With excessive and wrong agitation there is always a risk of an emulsion forming, which should not normally happen with strong lye.

The amount of excess lye required depends not only on the quantity and type of impurities, but also on the extent of de-acidification aimed at. For oils and fats for edible purposes, when the f.f.a. percentage should not exceed 0·05 per cent, a relatively higher excess is required than when a maximum acidity of 0·1–0·2 per cent is satisfactory. The latter is often the case with cottonseed oil, when at the oil mills impurities and most of the free fatty acids are removed in the form of a blackish soapstock before the oil is stored or dispatched to refineries. This kind of oil, generally referred to as "washed" cotton-oil, has usually a residual acidity of 0·1–0·2 per cent, and is given a final neutralization at the plant, where it is used for edible fat, or it can be directly used for hydrogenation. The result of the neutralization is determined by titration and, if necessary, additional caustic is added.

The strong caustic lye refining technique varies a little in the different refineries, and in some cases refiners claim to have some secret prodecure, but generally the following methods are the principal ones:

In a cylindrical vessel with conical bottom—for description of plant see later—the oil is mixed at a temperature of 20–30°C (or higher if the melting-point of the fat necessitates it) with caustic soda lye of the chosen strength and excess. If the vessel is constructed for working under vacuum the oil can be de-aerated by keeping it under vacuum for a time; otherwise it is advisable to let any air bubbles from pumping and filling escape from the oil before treatment. This will help to prevent floating soapstock. The caustic solution is then added via a spray-pipe while the oil is being vigorously stirred. This addition may take 10–20 min., and when the caustic is thoroughly mixed with the oil, stirring is slowed down to a speed which will just keep the contents well mixed, and the temperature is gradually raised by use of closed steam coils or heating jackets to about 60°C as quickly as possible. The "break" will then take place and soap particles form and separate from the oil. They gradually increase in size through aggregation under the influence of slow stirring, and when they show a tendency to settle, heating and stirring is stopped and the mixture left for settling. With the right technique this only takes a few hours, and the gradual cooling helps to firm up the concentrated soapstock and makes it separate without emulsion from the clear neutral supernatant oil. This is then decanted or skimmed off the soapstock by means of a swivel pipe, and by suitable adjustment of the intake of this pipe, combined with occasional slow stirring for a few minutes, satisfactory segregation of neutral oil and residue can be achieved. If the oil is to be stored it requires drying and filtration to remove small traces of soap and moisture, which might induce hydrolysis during storage. If required for hydrogenation and adsorption bleaching these treatments will deal with traces of soap and moisture. The semi-solid soapstock may require heating to make it flow easily through the drain cock or slide valve at the bottom of the neutralization vessel.

In another method the crude oil is warmed in the vessel by closed steam coils to 48–50°C and then by direct steam through the oil to 60°C, whilst the oil is stirred. Caustic lye of 15°Bé and at a temperature of 80°C is sprayed on the oil through a perforated pipe in an amount equal to about 1·75 times the theoretical quantity. Stirring is continued until the "break" occurs, and the oil is then left for settling 5–10 min. Boiling water equal to about 10 per cent of the weight of the oil is then sprayed on the oil without agitation and the contents of the vessel left to settle. After about 2 hours the oil can be drawn off through the swivel pipe and the soapstock drained off. The neutralized oil is run to a wash vessel, heated to 65°C with open steam, and a further quantity of caustic lye of 10°Bé equal to 25 per cent of the original theoretical amount for neutralization is stirred into the oil. After being left a few minutes for settling a rain of boiling water, equal to about 10 per cent of the oil is sprayed on and run through the oil. The thin soap solution is settled and drained, and further washes with boiling water given, if necessary, to remove traces of soap. This treatment should reduce the acidity in the oil to less than 0·05 per cent, and it is now ready for drying and bleaching. It will be realized that the soapstocks by this method are more dilute.

A modification of this method, often applied to cottonseed oils, provides for the addition to the oil at 50°C of caustic lye of 18°Bé in an excess of 100 per cent while stirring continues for 20–30 min. till the "break" takes place. After stopping the stirrer about 10 per cent water of 50°C is added and settling takes place in about 1 hour. After draining off the soapstock two or three washes with 10 per cent of very dilute lye—0·4 per cent strength—of 100°C are given, followed by draining, and after the last dilute caustic wash the oil is heated to 95°C and washed two or three times with boiling water, 8–10 per cent each time. The whole treatment will take 10–12 hours.

A method, in which caustic lye containing salt is used, is as follows: Crude oil is heated under stirring to 70–80°C and caustic lye of 20°Bé containing 5 per cent salt and heated to 90°C is sprayed on the oil in an excess of 40–100 per cent according to the quality of the crude oil. Stirring is continued for 1–1½ hours while the soap clots are broken up. Stirring is then stopped and 15–20 per cent boiling water showered on. After settling the soap solution the clear supernatant oil is decanted off to a wash tank. This treatment takes 6–7 hours and is, if necessary, followed by several water washes in the wash tank.

Sometimes, when dealing with oils which do not respond to the usual treatment without excessive losses, it is useful to add after the caustic some auxiliary chemical, which helps the "break" and compacts the soap without occluding excessive amounts of neutral oil. Apart from salt, already mentioned, good results have been obtained with the addition at 80–85°C of 1 per cent of a 10 per cent soda ash solution mixed with the same amount of sodium silicate solution. DRESSLER[26] recommends using at 27°C caustic lye of 15°Bé, while stirring rapidly, and follow immediately with 0·3 per cent sodium silicate in 4 per cent solution, stirring continuously for one hour. The mixture is then heated to about 44°C, while stirring slowly, and 5–8 per cent cold water sprayed on the surface. The soap on breaking settles rapidly. DRESSLER also mentions the use, in combination, of soda and ash and silicate, a procedure that is particularly effective in the dilute lye process.

A vacuum neutralization process has been recommended by E. BATAILLE and adopted in a number of refineries. In his process the mixture of caustic lye and crude oil is vigorously agitated in a horizontal jacketed cylindrical vessel under vacuum, and the water from the soap solution evaporated in course of 2–3 hours at a temperature corresponding to the vapour pressure of water at the vacuum obtained; superheating causes frothing. The lively steam development and mixing cause a rapid and complete reaction with little excess of lye, and the dry granular soap settles without causing emulsions and in such a form that very little neutral oil is occluded. Oil and soapstock are run to a vertical cylindrical tank with conical bottom, the soapstock settled and the neutral oil decanted off. The soapstock is then heated and salted out and finally drained from the last remnants of neutral oil.

Neutralization with Dilute Caustic Alkali

This method is very widely used in Europe, as it can be applied to all oils and fats, even to cottonseed oil from undecorticated seed; however, as mentioned, the ultimate utilization of the soapstock has to be considered. When carried out with proper precautions it entails a smaller loss of neutral oil than the "batch" or "kettle" process with strong caustic lye, but special technique and skill is required to prevent formation of emulsions, to which the large quantities of water, and consequently thin soap and mucilage solutions, in many cases tend.

Although the dilute caustic lye for this method is usually of less strength than 5°Bé (3·35 per cent or 0·75 normal), several modifications use a much stronger lye, 12–18°Bé, for addition to the crude oil and effect the dilution in the neutralizing vessel in course of the process, with the result that the soapstock forms a thin solution before it is separated from the neutralized oil. The method is less suitable for crude oils with a high acidity (6 per cent f.f.a. or more) as the volume of dilute lye would be too large. By carefully adjusting the technique to the particular supply of crude oil loss of neutral oil by over-saponification or by emulsifying it into the soap solution can largely be avoided, thus minimizing refining losses.

The soap solution, because of its fluidity even at low temperature, can easily be drained from the supernatant oil. If the process is applied to a non-de-gummed oil, a layer of impurities and soap is often formed between the clear soap solution and the neutral oil, and great precautions are necessary to avoid an emulsion forming which will occlude large quantities of neutral oil. A de-gumming treatment is therefore often applied to oils intended for this process; there are, however, modifications of the process which make a pre-treatment unnecessary.

A dilute soap solution is quite effective in dissolving gums and colouring matters, and if neutralization is manipulated in such a way that a colloidal soap solution is formed, which easily separates from the oil, purification and neutralization can be achieved with an insignificant loss of enmeshed oil in the soap. Subsidiary treatments are often applied as part of the dilute lye process, the object being to bring down or grain out soap or mucilage dissolved colloidally in the oil. Such treatments may be washes with hot water, very dilute caustic soda, salt brine solution, soda ash or alkaline silicate. While to avoid emulsification stirring should never be fast, it should be fast enough to ensure good contact of alkali with the whole volume of oil, as slow passage of caustic through the oil may, if the caustic is for a short time present in excess, cause over-saponification and later formation of acid soaps, if sinking through layers of unneutralized oil. Conditions for holding the impurities in colloidal suspension in the soap solution are then unfavourable and emulsions may be formed, particularly if the oil contains some partial glycerides such as mono and diglycerides.

The process can be carried out in such a way that purification and neutralization take place at the same time, or the impurities can be removed after neutralization. In the first case the emphasis is on the formation of a homogeneous soap solution, which will dissolve the impurities. Many of these dissolve colloidally in water at 40–50°C, but coagulate at temperatures above 85°C. This behaviour is made use of in the hydration de-gumming pre-treatment, but if the caustic lye is added rapidly and with the right degree of stirring, a soap solution containing the impurities will form and can be easily settled with little risk of emulsion formation.

In certain oils there may be a relatively high proportion of phosphatides which, if oxidized and deteriorated in quality, tend to cause an emulsion layer to form at the interface of the soap solution and the oil, because they have lost their power to hydrate and dissolve in water or lye; they may even remain in colloidal solution in the oil. In such cases an after-treatment is often given after the soap solution, but not the emulsion, has been drained off. Such an after-treatment may be with a solution of sodium silicate, which when it flocculates in the oil absorbs and precipitates the impurities left in the oil.

For the success of the various modifications of the dilute caustic lye method it is important to be able to control the degree of stirring, and it should be possible to reduce speed to 30 r.p.m. Temperature control as well as the method and rate of addition of the various ingredients and solutions is important.

Some examples will show the application of the mentioned general principles of the dilute caustic lye method:

Crude oil, while being stirred, is heated to about 95°C. Stirring is then stopped and lye of 4°Bé and at a temperature of 98–100°C is rained on the top of the oil by means of a suitable arrangement so that a fine spray of small droplets covers the whole surface. It is important that the lye temperature is slightly higher than that of the oil, as this helps to prevent formation of emulsions. The excess of lye may be higher by this method than when strong lye is used. The degree of neutralization is ascertained by titration and if necessary more lye is sprayed on. When the oil is neutral, hot water or a weak salt solution is sprayed on the quiescent oil to dissolve and wash down remnants of soap in the oil. After an hour's settling the soap solution should be ready for draining. By correct operation there is a fairly complete separation of oil and soap solution. There may at times be a small layer of an emulsion of neutral oil in soap solution at the interface. The clear soap solution is drawn off to a vat for treatment with mineral acid to recover the fatty matter from the soap as the so-called "acid oil" (see p. 70). If there is an emulsion layer, it is run to a separate vat for treatment for recovery of the neutral oil it contains; generally the emulsion layers from a number of refining batches are collected, and when a suitable quantity has been accumulated, it is boiled up with direct steam and treated with salt, which causes the neutral oil to separate from the soap solution. The former is added to the next batch of crude oil, the latter to the main soap solutions for recovery of "acid oil". The amount of neutral oil lost with the "acid oil" is generally less than 10 per cent of the latter.

Crude oil, if rather high in f.f.a. content, would require a large volume of dilute alkali for neutralization; this can therefore better be carried out in several steps of partial neutralization. For instance, an oil with 7·5 per cent f.f.a. would require a volume of 4°Bé caustic soda equal to about 40 per cent of the oil volume, plus any excess required. Oils of higher f.f.a. content would require correspondingly more. It would be impractical to work with such large quantities in one operation. Many refiners would, however, adopt other methods, depending on the type of oil or fat.

A dilute lye method, frequently used for oils and fats which contain only insignificant amounts of partial glycerides, is as follows: The oil is heated to about 98°C and the theoretical quantity of caustic soda solution of 5°Bé strength plus an excess corresponding to 0·5–1·0 per cent f.f.a. is added while the oil is gently stirred. When all the lye has been added the agitators are stopped and about 10 per cent of caustic soda solution of 0·4 per cent strength (deci-normal) is sprayed on the oil. This is then left to settle and the soap solution drained off. A hot water wash with 10 per cent water is given to the oil and after draining followed by a wash with 10 per cent of a 0·4 per cent caustic soda solution, while steam is being blown through the mixture. After settling and draining, one or more hot water washes with 10 per cent water are given until the oil is free from soap.

There are many slight variations of this method in accordance with the f.f.a. content and general quality of the crude oil. If, for instance, the crude material is a hydrogenated fat of low f.f.a. content, 0·3 per cent or less, the treatment may simply be a wash with a slight excess of deci-normal caustic soda, followed by washes with hot water.

Neutralization with Mixed Concentrations of Caustic Lye

To carry out the combined de-gumming and neutralization and make use of the colloidal solubility of mucilage in water under 50°C some refiners prefer to add to the oil, before neutralization, a certain amount of water of a temperature above the melting-point of the fatty matter, but not exceeding 50°C. In some refineries about 30 per cent water is used, calculated on the amount of oil, and after good mixing the caustic lye in the theoretical amount plus 10 per cent excess is added in the form of a solution of 18–20°Bé. By dilution with the water already added this becomes a dilute lye. Other refineries base the amount of water, initially added, on the percentage of f.f.a.

in the oil, for instance 2–5 times the amount of free fatty acids. This is added under vigorous stirring and the temperature increased to 85–90°C in course of about one hour. Caustic lye of 20Bé is added in an excess of 10–20 per cent and stirring discontinued to allow the soap solution to settle and be drained off after a couple of hours. A wash with 10 per cent deci-normal caustic lye follows, and, after draining, 2 or 3 washes with hot water until the oil is free from soap.

Some oils contain substances which are not soluble in the dilute neutral soap solution, and which may form an emulsion layer between the soap solution and the oil, or may remain dissolved in the oil. They are frequently soluble in weak alkali solutions and are therefore, after the soap is removed, dissolved in the washes with deci-normal caustic or in an additional wash with 2–5 per cent of a boiling soda ash solution of 10 per cent strength, followed by hot water washes. These weak alkali solutions entail no risk of over-saponification.

Where crude oils contain a relatively high percentage of phosphatides and mucilage, there may in spite of all precautions be a tendency for a layer of emulsion to form at the interface. In that case the soap solution is drained off, but the emulsion layer is retained and together with the neutralized oil treated with a solution of alkaline sodium silicate. The flocculation of the hydrated silica causes preferential absorption of the mucilage in the alkaline solution and an efficient separation of this solution and oil. For instance, oil is neutralized at 90–95°C with dilute caustic lye of 5°Bé in slight excess and under moderate stirring. The soap solution is drained off after settling, but any emulsion layer which may have formed is retained. The contents of the vessel are stirred, and if an emulsion is formed, a little salt is added to break it. While stirring is continued about 2·5 per cent of a hot soda ash solution of 20 per cent strength is added at about 100°C, and immediately afterwards 1 per cent of a solution of equal parts of waterglass of 40°Bé and water. Stirring is now intensified by blowing steam through the mixture for about 15 mins. Stirring is then stopped, 2·5 per cent hot water sprayed on and the contents of the vessel allowed to settle. In course of 1–1·5 hours settling should be complete, and initially a sludge of hydrated silica and mucilage is drained off, followed by a clear soda ash solution. After draining the oil is washed twice with 8–10 per cent hot water.

This type of treatment is frequently used with cottonseed oil of African origin. The first step is neutralization at 50°C with the theoretical amount of caustic soda solution of 4°–6°Bé plus sufficient excess for 1 per cent f.f.a. The oil is stirred vigorously during and for a few minutes after the addition of caustic. The rate of stirring is then reduced and the oil gradually heated by indirect steam to 80°C, when stirring ceases and 3–4 per cent boiling water is sprayed on. The oil is left to settle and in due course the soap is drained off. The second step is to reduce the colouring matter by means of caustic soda. The neutral oil is heated by indirect steam to 95–98°C and then boiled up by blowing steam through, while at the same time a caustic soda lye of 6°Bé, equivalent to 1 per cent f.f.a., is added. This is followed by 0·3 per cent of a boiling sodium silicate solution. Stirring and steaming is now stopped and 10 per cent boiling water sprayed on. The contents are settled and the watery solution drained off. The final step is a cleaning up of the oil by boiling it up with direct steam, adding successively 1–2 per cent of a hot 10 per cent soda ash solution and 1 per cent of a hot sodium silicate solution. After a few minutes the steam is turned off and the oil sprayed with 10 per cent of boiling water and settled in about an hour, when the washes should be ready to be drained off.

The dilute lye method can be applied to most crude oils and fats which are considered suitable for conversion into edible fats. Experience and skill may suggest many minor changes in the methods described, which merely indicate the underlying principles. Difficulties may arise with raw materials of high acidity, 6–7 per cent or more, and of relatively high content of partly hydrolyzed glycerides, such as mono and diglycerides. In such cases it is frequently an advantage to salt out the soap by using ordinary salt as addition to the caustic soda lye in proportions that will ensure graining of the soap. The temperature of the treatment should only be moderate, 50°C or less, as there is otherwise a tendency for over-saponification to take place, particularly in the presence of partial glycerides. The caustic lye contains about 10 per cent caustic soda and about 10 per cent salt. The crude oil is heated to 50°C and de-aerated in vacuum, as released air bubbles may cause a soap scum and prevent settling of the soap. A slight excess of lye is added while the oil is being well agitated, and the temperature is gradually increased until flocculation or " break " takes place at about 85°C. The oil is then left to settle, which may take a couple of hours. Boiling water to the extent of 5 per cent is sprayed on the oil and left to settle. The watery solution can now be drained off, brine being the first to run away and then soap. The oil is usually given two more washes with 5 per cent boiling water, with settling and draining, and sometimes a wash with 2 per cent of a soda ash solution of 10 per cent strength is given in place of, or additional to, water washing.

Plant for Alkali Neutralization by the Batch Process

Neutralization with alkaline lyes is carried out in open or closed vessels, vertical cylindrical steel vats, often called "kettles", the cylindrical part being 2–2½ times the diameter, the angle at the apex of the cone about 90° to get the best slope for draining. Some vessels are provided with a steam jacket round the lower half and the cone, but to obtain more rapid control of temperature changes most vessels are fitted with internal coils for steam heating, or with both jackets and coils. Various systems of heating coils are used, such as helical coils or vertical coils connecting circular headers. A perforated steam distributing coil at the bottom should be provided for methods where a supply of direct steam is wanted. The vessels are provided with stirrers, the types varying according to the maker's ideas of construction, but the

49

essential point is, that they should give effective mixing without excessive emulsification or centrifugal effect. They should preferably be arranged with variable speed, as at times slow stirring is required. Closed neutralizers, particularly if they are also used for adsorption bleaching, the so-called neutralizer-bleachers, should be constructed to operate under vacuum, and if used for bleaching with adsorbents the stirrer should reach right down into the cone. A device should be arranged at the top, in the form of a circular perforated pipe or spray nozzles, for efficient and uniform distribution of the alkali and other liquids over the surface in a comparatively short time, preferably less than 15 mins. It is useful to have one or two sampling cocks some distance from the bottom outlet to obtain indication of the separation of the layers during settling and draining.

Fig. 30 shows front and top views and a vertical section of an open top neutralizer. The cone and the lower part of the cylinder is provided with a heating jacket for steam at 2–3 atm. pressure. A grid-stirrer revolving at a speed of about 30 r.p.m. effects the mixing without beating up the soap. Spray nozzles are fitted on a circular pipe at the top, and this can rotate independently of the agitator, which is claimed to be of special advantage when the device is used for spraying dilute lye on the quiescent oil. When strong lyes are used agitator and nozzles revolve together. An arrangement at the top allows wash-waters, etc., to enter the spraying system. The vessel is fitted with a scale to indicate contents. At the bottom of the cylindrical part is the oil outlet, connected to a swivel-jointed pipe through which, if desired, the neutralized oil can be removed to a separate wash vessel. The swivel-pipe inlet is during neutralization closed by a plug which can be manipulated from the top. The jacket is also arranged for cooling with water. Soapstock is removed through the bottom valve.

Fig. 31 shows a vertical section of another open neutralizer. In this the heating jacket covers only the conical part and is used principally for increasing the fluidity of the soapstock for draining. A cylindrical nest of vertical steam pipes between top and bottom headers permits temperature control of the contents. The paddle stirrer is driven by a variable speed motor, and plates for breaking froth are fitted on the shaft at the oil surface. A circular pipe at the top with spray nozzles permits a fine distribution of the alkali. The vessel is fitted with a swing pipe with swivel joint for decanting off the neutralized oil after settling of the soapstock. When working with concentrations of alkali which allow easy draining of the soapstock before the neutral oil is removed, this vessel can also be used for washing the oil free from soap.

Other open neutralizers have coil spirals for heating or cooling, stirrers of the gate type, propellers or helical screws. Neutral oil may be drained off through the bottom valve after draining off soap solution and wash waters.

Many refiners use closed neutralizers, arranged to work under vacuum if desired. Although neutralization is generally done at atmospheric pressure, these vessels permit a preliminary de-aeration under vacuum, which is often a useful preliminary to neutralization, and also, when the oil is neutralized and washed, vacuum drying and bleaching, where separate vessels for that purpose are not available. As a matter of fact, so-called neutralizer-bleachers

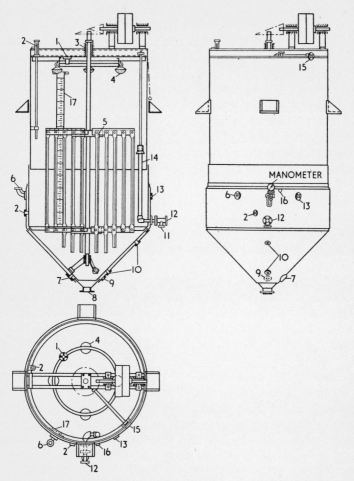

Fig. 30. Open-top neutraliser, according to *Harburger Eisen- u Bronzewerke*.

1. Wash-water inlet.	7. Water outlet.	13. Steam inlet.
2. Thermometer.	8. Soapstock outlet.	14. Swivel pipe.
3. Ball bearing.	9. Condensate outlet.	15. Lye inlet.
4. Spray.	10. Sampling cocks.	16. Vent.
5. Stirrer.	11. Sample outlet.	17. Content scale.
6. Safety valve.	12. Oil outlet.	

are now widely used. Certain oils which contain valuable substances very susceptible to oxidation, such as liver oils rich in vitamins and carotene-containing oils, are frequently neutralized in vacuum-vessels.

Fig. 32 shows a closed neutralizer-bleacher, designed for working under vacuum, if required. It has a set of vertical pipes, with top and bottom headers, for heating and cooling, and a steam-heated jacket round the conical bottom. A paddle stirrer driven by a variable speed motor provides the necessary agitation and mixing. Lye and other solutions are admitted

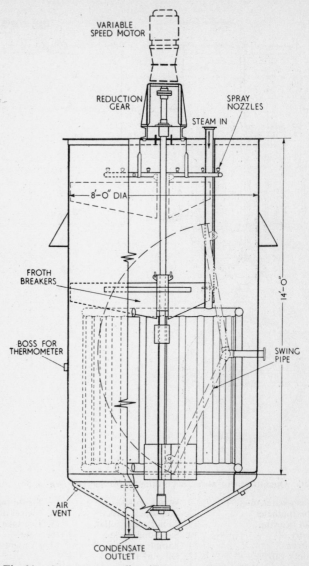

Fig. 31. Open-top neutraliser (Courtesy: *Bamag Ltd., London*).

through a perforated circular pipe under the cover, and from the perforations fall on to splash-plates which distribute the liquids as a fine spray on the surface of the oil. The connection to the vacuum system is on the cover and is provided with a baffle deflector plate. An inlet pipe for bleaching earth through the cover is carried well down below the level of the baffle plate to prevent the fine powdery earth being sucked out. Sight glasses are provided on the top and at the side.

As with the open neutralizers, there are also many variations of details in

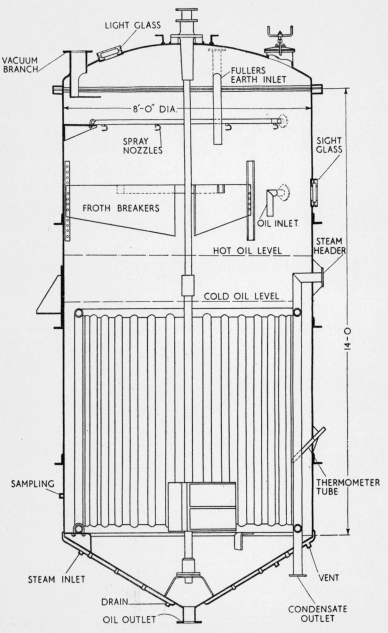

Fig. 32. Vacuum Neutraliser-Bleacher (Courtesy: *Bamag Ltd., London*).

53

the closed vessels, different constructions of stirrers, spray arrangements, heating coils, etc. Where the vessel is used as a neutralizer-bleacher, refiners often prefer the heating means as nests of vertical pipes, as bleaching earth may show less tendency to be retained on the pipes when the vessel is emptied after bleaching.

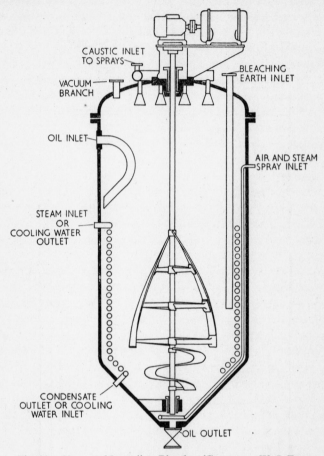

Fig. 33. Vacuum Neutraliser-Bleacher (Courtesy: *W. J. Fraser & Co. Ltd., Dagenham*).

Fig. 33 shows in section a slightly different closed vacuum neutralizer-bleacher. It has no heating jacket, the temperature being controlled by helical coils for steam or water. The stirrer, driven by a variable speed motor, is of the "gate" type with the connecting bars between the upper and lower radial arms, which are recessed at angles of 90°, forming screw planes. A special helical extension blade on the stirrer reaches well down into the cone to prevent premature settling. The circular pipe for admitting lye and other liquids is outside the top with branch pipes passing through the cover to nozzles and splash-plates inside; this arrangement is claimed to facilitate cleaning of the distribution system. The inlet pipe for bleaching earth is carried down to a level well below the surface of the oil, thus preventing loss of dust particles when drawing in the earth by vacuum. Direct steam for boiling up the contents, or a supply of air, can be admitted through a pipe terminating in a perforated distribution coil at the bottom of the cone.

Caustic soda is received either in tank waggons, and can then be pumped to an iron storage tank for strong caustic, or in iron drums, which are placed in an iron tank with cover, where the solid caustic soda is dissolved in water heated by direct steam, after the bottom has been removed from the drums. If the dissolving tank is arranged for pressure, air can be used for blowing the caustic to the storage tank. Various supply and measuring tanks for caustic lye and other solutions should be so dimensioned that the required ingredients can be supplied, either by gravity or under pressure, to the neutralizers in minimum time to expedite the process.

De-acidification by neutralization of the free fatty acid with caustic lye leaves usually, after the soap solution has been removed, a small quantity of soap in solution or very fine suspension in the oil; this is removed by washes with hot water and frequently two, three or more washes are necessary before the oil is free from soap, as shown by the absence of an alkaline reaction in the wash-water. The washing, as already described, is either done under stirring of the mixture or by raining the water on to the oil as a fine spray. In the first wash, when about 0·2 per cent soap may be present, there is sometimes a tendency to emulsion formation. This can be avoided by using a weak salt solution in the first wash. In recent years, to save time taken by settling and repeated washes, the neutralized oil mixed with the wash-water is often run through a high-speed centrifuge for efficient separation.

Where the washing and final drying of the neutralized oil is done in a separate apparatus, this is similar in construction to a neutralizer-bleacher, or it may be of the simpler design shown in Fig. 34, where the vessel has no internal heating coils and a rather plain stirrer; circulation baffles are fitted to the cylindrical wall and a circular pipe at the top with nozzles for distribution of the wash solutions. There is a vacuum connection at the top and the oil is often drawn in by placing the vessel under vacuum, but the washing operations are carried out at atmospheric pressure. After settling and separation in the vessel the wash-waters are drained off from the bottom and passed through settling and trapping tanks to trap traces of fat before the waters are run away. After washing is finished and waters drained off, the oil is kept hot (70°–90°C) and vacuum applied to the vessel to dry the oil. This must be done gradually and carefully to avoid frothing by the released steam bubbles, and a vent is provided for helping to control frothing. When this ceases, which can be seen in the inspection glass, the oil will be dry and show a clear limpid appearance.

When planning a refinery the question often arises whether to choose open or closed neutralizing vessels, separate washing and bleaching, etc., and no hard and fast rule can be laid down as to the best plant to adopt.

It depends on many factors, such as types of raw material, methods chosen, disposal of soapstock, time cycles of operations, space available, etc. Each case has therefore to be considered as a separate problem.

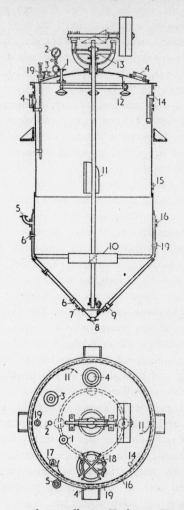

Fig. 34. Washing vessel, according to *Harburger Eisen- u Bronzewerke.*

1. Water inlet.
2. Vacuum gauge.
3. Vacuum connection.
4. Observation glass.
5. Safety valve.
6. Sampling cocks.
7. Condensate outlet from jacket.
8. Water outlet.
9. Oil outlet.
10. Stirrer.
11. Circulation baffle.
12. Spray.
13. Ball bearing.
14. Oil inlet.
15. Oil level indicator.
16. Steam inlet for jacket.
17. Vent.
18. Manhole.
19. Thermometer.

Continuous Neutralization Processes

Although in the early days of refining continuous methods of neutralizing with alkali were proposed—for instance continuous mixing of lye and oil in centrifugal emulsors with subsequent centrifugal separation (*De Laval, Ekenberg*), or continuous mixing of oil and lye containing salt in steam jets, followed by settling—they have not gained practical importance until the methods and plants proposed by *The Sharples Specialty Co.*[27], by *Clayton and Refining Inc.*[28], and by the *De Laval Separator Co.* were introduced. The wide range of oils and fats, used in Europe, and the variations in the quality of the crude materials demand frequent flexibility and changes in the refining methods, whereas the narrower range in types of oils used in U.S.A. combined with a generally larger scale of operations provided a fertile ground for development of standardised continuous working. In recent years, however, the range of materials which can be successfully and economically treated by the continuous plant has been considerably extended and flexibility increased, with the result that also in Europe the continuous neutralizing plant is being adopted.

Apart from the advantages of working a continuous process, the much reduced refining losses, which resulted from the use of the continuous centrifugal method in U.S.A., when working to the standards required there for subsequent successful treatment of the oil, made the change from batch to continuous methods economically advantageous. In Europe, however, the efficient refiners had already developed, on the fats and oils generally available, methods which gave refining efficiencies permitting little or no improvement by the continuous centrifugal process, and a change to this newer method and expensive plant could in many cases only be considered when the question of new installations arose. In view of the considerable difference in value of refined oil and by-products from refining, the need for avoiding excessive losses is obvious, and the modern continuous plant will no doubt play an important part in this direction and prove an economic investment to many refiners.

A semi-continuous process combining batch neutralization with continuous centrifugal separation of soapstock and wash-water has been introduced by the *De Laval Co. Ltd.*, and is particularly recommended for smaller refineries dealing with a number of oils and fats. The flow sheet in Fig. 35 shows that the plant consists of two cylindrical neutralizing vessels *4* fitted with agitators and having conical bottoms. Crude oil is pumped in by *1* and lye supplied by gravity from tank *2* and distribution pipe *3*. Neutralization is at low temperature, and the agitators run fairly fast while the lye is being added. Stirring is then slowed down for the "break", but should be sufficient to keep the soap particles in even suspension, while the contents are drawn off from the bottom and passed through a heater *6* with thermometers *5* and *7* to show the increase in temperature. The oil-soap mixture is in contact at the higher temperature for only a few seconds before being passed to the centrifugal soapstock separators *8*, from which the soap solution runs to the splitting tank for acid treatment, while the neutral oil is mixed with a stream of hot water from tank *11* and pumped through wash-tank *12* to wash-water separators *13*. The wash-water is discharged to waste or to splitting tanks, whereas the oil by pump *14* is passed to vacuum vessels for flash evaporation of traces of moisture before bleaching. While excess and strength of lye as well as neutralization temperature depends on circumstances, they should be chosen so that the soapstock is sufficiently fluid to flow from the centrifuges, and so that there should be a good "break" of soap from oil. Under the right conditions the neutral oil will contain less than 0·2 per cent moisture and only a trace of soap. While the contents of one vessel is separated another is used for neutralization, thus keeping the separators in continuous use. In the washing tanks about 20 per cent hot water is used, and after separation in the secondary centrifuges the oil is free from soap; it still contains about 0·2 per cent moisture, which is removed in the vacuum evaporator. It is claimed that the refining loss is 20–30 per cent less than by the conventional batch process

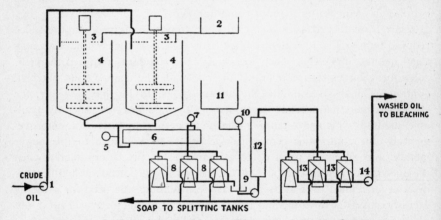

Fig. 35. Semi-continuous cold neutralising process, De Laval system.

owing to the better separation of oil from soapstock, the absence of emulsion layers and elimination of the risk of over-saponification. The following figures show the difference in losses by the batch process with gravity settling and the semi-continuous process, as obtained by the makers of the plant.

f.f.a. Content of crude oil		Loss, gravity settling		Loss, semi-continuous process
2·20%	·	4·86%	·	3·60%
4·81%	·	11·01%	·	8·38%
3·05%	·	7·01%	·	4·70%

In the original continuous neutralization process, proposed by the *Sharples Specialty Company* and described by JAMES[29], strong caustic soda lye and oil were passed by adjustable proportioning pumps through a continuous mixer-emulsifier and a heater, where the mixture was heated to about 60°C for the "break", to centrifugal separators of the Sharples Supercentrifuge type for the separation of neutralized oil and soapstock, the total contact period of oil and caustic lye being only 3 minutes, thus minimizing the risk

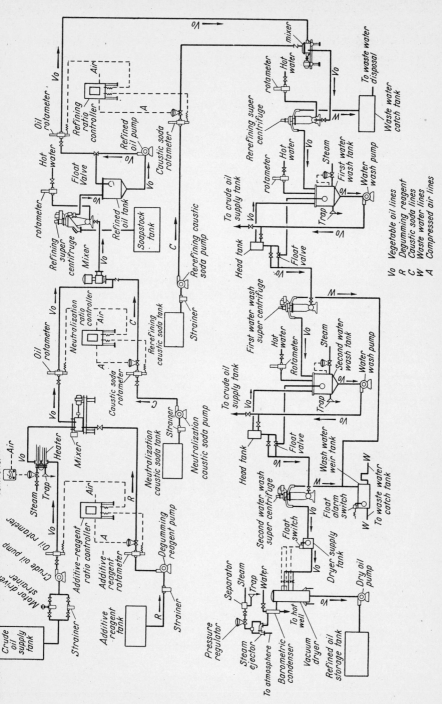

Fig. 36. Sharples continuous caustic lye process.

Vo   Vegetable oil lines
R   Degumming reagent
C   Caustic soda lines
W   Waste water lines
A   Compressed air lines

of over-saponification in spite of an excess of caustic being used. The soap-stock was discharged through the sludge outlets from the centrifuges while the neutralized oil, containing a trace of soap and moisture in suspension, was pumped to a wash tank, where it was mixed with 10–15 per cent hot water of 75–80°C and passed through a secondary centrifuge, from which a practically soap-free neutral oil was obtained, while the wash-water was run to waste or to heat interchangers. In some refineries a second washing process with similar washing and separating arrangements was carried out before the oil with a moisture content of 0·2–0·3 per cent was passed to continuous vacuum flash evaporators for drying the oil.

Since that original process, which claimed to save about 30 per cent of the refining loss compared with the batch process, was proposed, further modifications have been introduced to improve yield and quality, such as the use of "additives" in the form of organic acids, for instance citric acid, to assist de-gumming, and a secondary caustic soda treatment of the already neutralized oil to improve the colour. The improved method, indicated diagrammatically in the flow-sheet in Fig. 36, is as follows: The crude oil, after being strained, is pumped through a rotameter and a tubular heater, where it is heated to about 60°C, to a mixer where a small quantity, 0·03–0·1 per cent, of "additive" or de-gumming reagent is mixed in, the proportion being maintained by the "ratio controller". This "additive" conditions the gums for easier removal by the subsequent caustic lye treatment. From the first mixer the conditioned oil joins a stream of caustic soda of 20°–28°Bé which is added in the theoretical quantity for neutralization and is controlled for the correct ratio by a special device. The oil-caustic flow passes then through a short-contact mixer where neutralization takes place, and the oil-soap mixture enters a Sludge Discharge Supercentrifuge which through the sludge outlet discharges the soapstock to the soapstock tank, and through the other outlet the neutralized oil to a "refined oil" buffer tank.

The Sharples Super centrifuge is of the hollow cylindrical rotor type with the rotor revolving at about 15,000 r.p.m. The mixture enters at the bottom and is guided towards the top by three-wing vanes while separation takes place and two cylindrical layers are formed, which leave through separate adjustable discharge openings leading to the discharge ports. The centrifuges used for soapstock separation are constructed specially to deal with the heavy sludge which is discharged into part of the frame that slopes towards an outlet of large diameter (Fig. 37).

Both the centrifuge for soapstock separation and the re-refine centrifuge, used in the next step in the process, have arrangements for the addition of some hot water, sometimes with a little salt or sodium sulphate added, at the bottom inlet to ensure, if necessary, a sharper separation of the oil from the aqueous phase.

The oil, separated from the soapstock, is pumped to a mixer for the so-called re-refining treatment, which consists in adding to the neutralized oil a further small quantity of caustic lye. This improves the colour of the oil

Fig. 37.   Sharples Super-centrifuge with sludge discharge
(Courtesy: *The Sharples Corporation*).

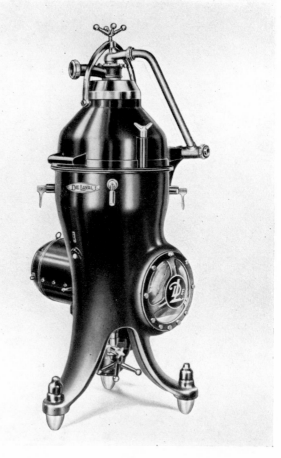

Fig. 39.   De Laval hermetic soapstock separator
(Courtesy: *Alfa-Laval Co. Ltd., London*).

and removes any small traces of free fatty acids which may be present after the neutralization treatment with the theoretical amount of lye. The risk of over-saponification is negligible as the principal condition for this, viz. the

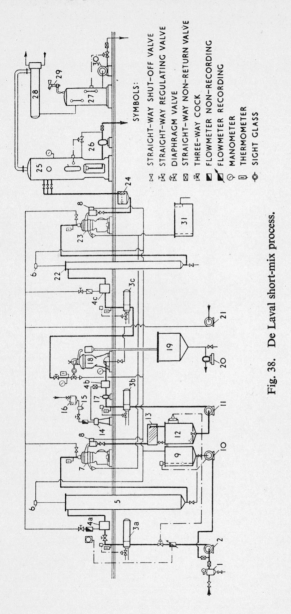

SYMBOLS:

⊠ STRAIGHT-WAY SHUT-OFF VALVE
⊠ STRAIGHT-WAY REGULATING VALVE
⊠ DIAPHRAGM VALVE
⊠ STRAIGHT-WAY NON-RETURN VALVE
⊠ THREE-WAY COCK
◗ FLOWMETER NON-RECORDING
◖ FLOWMETER RECORDING
⊘ MANOMETER
▭ THERMOMETER
◇ SIGHT GLASS

Fig. 38. De Laval short-mix process.

presence of free fatty acids and soap, in addition to caustic, is practically absent. The re-refine mixture is separated in a second supercentrifuge of a slightly different design, as no heavy sludge is present; the waste alkali solution runs away through a catch-basin, while the re-refined oil, containing less than 0·05 per cent soap, passes to a first water-wash tank. Hot water, about 10 per cent, is added and the temperature of the mixture increased to to 75–80°C if desired. A circulation pump ensures an intimate mixing of the oil and water, which through a constant-head tank passes to the first wash-centrifuge. The water from here is run to waste via the catch basin, and the neutral washed oil is given a second similar wash treatment after which the soap content is less than 0·002 per cent. The moisture content is usually 0·4–0·5 per cent, as to separate in the centrifuge to a lower moisture content might entail losses of neutral oil. The final drying of the oil is done by flash evaporation in vacuum. It is claimed that this process gives a very high yield of neutralized oil; for instance, if the crude oil contains 97 per cent genuine glyceride, i.e., shows a "Wesson" loss of 3 per cent, the guaranteed yield is 95·6 per cent of the crude oil.

The *De Laval Separator Company's* continuous caustic soda process, based on the Clayton patents, effected the de-gumming, neutralizing and decolourizing as a combined operation, and after separation of soapstock and sludge in a special De Laval soapstock separator of the disc-centrifuge type the neutral oil was mixed with hot water and passed through secondary water-wash separators prior to drying of the oil by flash evaporation in a vacuum vessel.

Later the De Laval Short-Mix caustic soda process was developed to give greater flexibility where a number of different oils and fats are handled, and to obtain improvements in yields and quality by introducing a de-gumming pre-treatment, a very short contact period of caustic lye and de-gummed oil and centrifugal separation of neutralized oil in a hermetically closed separator.

A flow diagram illustrating the process is shown in Fig. 38. The crude oil after passing strainer *1* is pumped *2* through steam heater *3a* to mixer *4a* where a small percentage of hot water is added to hydrate the gums. The wetted oil passes under the pump pressure to the tall cylindrical tank *5*, where the gums flocculate and swell during the period of passage; the oil with sludge is then fed to the top of the De Laval sludge separator *7*, which discharges the sludge as a by-product, which from certain oils may be valuable if rich in lecithin, whereas the de-gummed oil via spout with overflow *8* runs to buffer tank *12* connected with de-aerating tank *13*. Pump *11* takes the oil via heater *3b*, where it is heated to about 80°C, and mixer pump *17* to the short-time neutralizer-mixer *4b* where in 2–3 secs. it is contacted and reacted with caustic lye from tank *16*, filter *15* and measuring device *14*. The oil-soap mixture then enters the special De Laval hermetic soapstock separator *18* (see Fig. 39 and Fig. 28) through the bottom of the central hollow axis under pressure and passes up to the disc separator bowl, where separation into soapstock and neutral oil takes place. The whole contact time in mixer and separator is only 30 secs. which lessens the risk of over-saponification. The soapstock leaves by the outlet spout and is collected in tank *19* while the neutral oil passes out through a closed pipe at the top without coming in contact with air. A regulating valve on the oil outlet pipe controls the degree of separation in the centrifuge. The neutralized oil under pressure is via a heater *3c* fed to mixer *4c*, where 10 per cent hot water is added, and through washing tank *22* the mixture is supplied to a water-wash separator *23* of the top-feed disc type, where the wash-water is discharged from one outlet to a catch basin *31* before running to waste, while the washed neutralized oil runs from the other outlet with overflow to a feed tank *24* and from there to the vacuum flash dryer *25*. The dry oil is continuously removed by pump *26* to storage or to the bleaching plant. Equipment *27–30* represents the vacuum and condensing plant. *21* is a pump for supplying hot water to the de-gumming and washing sections and, if required, to the centrifuges. *6* are overflow tanks which together with overflows *8* return overflow to emergency tank *9* from which pump *10* returns it to the crude oil supply. *20* is the pump for soapstock. Sometimes a step involving a caustic wash followed by appropriate centrifugal separation is interposed between neutralization and final hot water washing.

TABLE II. Typical commercial operating data with De Laval Short-Mix continuous refining plant

Type of oil	f.f.a. in crude (%)	Wesson loss (%)	Refining loss (%)	Refining factor	f.f.a. in acid oil (%)	f.f.a. in Neutralized oil (%)
Groundnut oil	0·62	—	0·81	1·30	80	0·04
„	2·44	3·2	4·14	1·71	75	0·03
„	5·80	—	7·95	1·37	75	0·03
Coconut oil	3·50	4·86	4·97	1·44	90	0·02
„	5·0	—	6·74	1·35	78	0·03
Rapeseed oil	1·4	1·7	1·9	1·37	82	0·08
„	1·7	2·0	3·06	1·80	75	0·06
Tallow	0·6	—	0·85	1·42	83	0·03
Soya bean oil	0·51	—	0·73	1·43	82	0·06
„	0·54	0·94	0·98	1·82	75	0·05
Palm oil	7·20	—	13·2	1·83	—	0·06

Table II gives data obtained with the De Laval Short-Mix process, as quoted by manufacturers. The refining factor is the ratio of loss to f.f.a. percentage in the crude oil. These favourable results are stated to be due to the initial de-gumming, which reduces risk of emulsion formation, to short contact time, which minimizes risk of over-saponification, and to keen separation of soap and oil through the special construction of the separators and the high neutralization temperature, which increases the fluidity of the phases.

Plants of this type are normally built for an output of 20–30 tons per 24 hours, but additional or larger units are available.

The continuous neutralization processes were first developed with caustic soda as the neutralizing reagent, the strength of the lye varying with the type and character of the oil, but generally between 14° and 28°Bé. A short time after their introduction they were extended to work with carbonate of soda. These processes will be described in a later section.

A different mixing technique in the continuous neutralization process has been proposed by R. H. FASH and is described in various patents.[30] He proposes to use a specially constructed centrifugal spray which converts oil and neutralizing reagent into separate mists and causes these to impinge and mix intimately on a cylindrical surface, from which the mixture is collected and subsequently separated into neutral oil and soapstock by means of centrifuges. The very fine comminution of the soap particles by the mist-mixing process and the large surface area of reaction caused in this manner is claimed to result in more effective colour reduction, a more rapid reaction, and a smaller loss of neutral oil because of the smaller excess of lye required. The mixing time is stated to be as short as 0·01 sec. and a stronger lye is therefore required. The patentee suggests 24°Bé (18 per cent) for a "slow breaking" cotton oil and 32°Bé (26 per cent) for a "fast breaking" oil and for soya bean oil. The heating up to "break" temperatures is done on the cylindrical surface and takes only 5 secs.; the period of contact and reaction before the centrifugal separation is therefore extremely short.

In the description in an earlier chapter of some of the methods of the dilute caustic lye process reference is made to the beneficial effect in many circumstances of silicate of soda as an ancillary ingredient. FASH also recognizes that in one of his patents, when he proposes to include sodium silicate or colloidal silica or both with his strong caustic solution for the mist-mixing process. The collected mixture of oil and soapstock is heated to 70–90°C and agitated to ensure good contact of oil with silicate in the soapstock, and while maintaining the temperature it is run through centrifuges for separation. The use of silicate is stated to reduce further the loss of neutral oil by its action on the soapstock oil-in-water type of emulsion, and to help in obtaining a better colour in the neutral oil.

Soapstock

Neutralization of the free fatty acids in crude oils and fats with alkali results in the formation of soaps; the separated soap solution is known as soapstock. The soapstock itself or the fatty matter it contains is used in the manufacture of soap or fatty acids. The fatty matter is partly combined with alkali as soap, partly some neutral oil absorbed in the soap during neutralization. If the soapstock is too dilute for economic transportation it is hydrolyzed or "split" by acidulation with mineral acid, usually sulphuric or hydrochloric acid, which causes separation of the fatty matter from the aqueous solution as a mixture of fatty acids and neutral fat. In Britain this mixture of fatty matters is known as "acid oil".

The reaction between the free fatty acids and the lye, as the result of the dispersion of the latter in the oil, leads to the formation of fine particles of soap which enclose droplets of oil. These are tenaciously retained as a disperse phase in the soap when by aggregation of the soap particles the "break" occurs and the soap separates from the continuous bulk oil phase. The soapstock that settles is therefore a mixture of soap, occluded neutral oil, unsaponifiable matter, colouring substances, mucilage, resin soaps, water, glycerine (derived from saponification of neutral oil), salt and other electrolytes, which may have been added during neutralization.

The content of soap and neutral oil in the soapstock varies widely, according to the method used for neutralization, and for economic reasons the refiner always endeavours to keep the neutral oil content as low as possible. THURMAN[23] has found semi-solid soapstock from the refining of cottonseed oil to contain on an average 18·7 per cent neutral oil, 26 per cent sodium soaps, 45·6 per cent water and 8·95 per cent non-fatty matter, or just over 40 per cent fatty matter. When dilute lye is used for neutralization, the fatty matter content of the soapstock may be as little as 10 per cent or less, of which the neutral oil may amount to a third to a tenth. The continuous caustic neutralization process generally gives soapstocks of 30–35 per cent fatty matter, of which a fifth or less is neutral oil.

Neutral oil that is held in the soapstock by adhesion, but not dispersed in the soap droplets, can to some extent be recovered by settling the soapstock hot for some time, when the oil floats to the surface and can be skimmed off. The dispersed neutral oil requires more elaborate treatment for recovery.

The physical nature of soapstock has been studied by SCHMIDT and MICHAILOWSKAJA[31], who have shown that the neutral oil in concentrated soapstock is dispersed as spherical particles of $1-4\mu$ radius. The size of these particles depends on the water and neutral oil content of the soapstock, as well as on the proportion of salt, mucilage, protein, partial glycerides, etc. The colloidal gums and proteins form films at the interface of the oil-globules and thus increase the stability of the emulsion. The temperature also affects the size of the oil particles. The type of emulsion, oil-in-water, is recognized by its dilution with water. In such emulsions AYERS[32] has found droplets of 0·002–0·02 mm diameter. In sufficiently diluted soapstock the smallest particles show Brownian movement.

If soapstock containing neutral oil is stored at elevated temperature in a tank the oil particles gradually float towards the surface, whereas the soap layer settles at the bottom; this separation can be speeded up by addition of salt. The speed of separation can be calculated on the basis of STOKES' law,

$$v = \frac{2g \cdot r^2(d_1 - d_2)}{9\eta},$$

65

where v is the speed of separation, g the acceleration due to gravity, r the radius of the oil spheres, d_1 the density of the sphere, d_2 the density of the surrounding medium and η the viscosity of the medium. If the soapstock contains 10 per cent neutral oil in the form of dispersed globules of radius 2μ, the speed of rise of the oil at 85°C would be 0·39 cm per hour. In a tank a few metres high it would thus take many days for the small particles from the bottom to rise to the surface.

As separation increases with the square of the globule radius, it can be speeded up by increasing the globule size, which can be done by diluting the

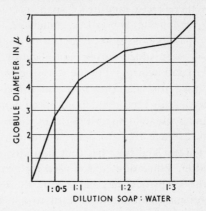

Fig. 40.   Change in oil-drop radius with dilution of soapstock.

soapstock. Fig. 40 shows the relation between average globule size and dilution. Similarly, increased neutral oil content tends to increase the size of the globules, as shown in the following table

Ratio of soap to fat	.	1:1	.	1:2	.	1:3	.	1:4
Largest diam. of glob.	.	$0·7\mu$	.	$1·41\mu$	.	$2·9\mu$	.	$4·4\mu$

STOKES' law shows that the speed of separation is directly proportional to the difference in density of the soap solution and the oil, and inversely to the viscosity of the former. The difference $(d_1 - d_2)$ depends on the temperature and the electrolyte content of the aqueous phase (e.g., salt) and on the ratio neutral oil:soap. The viscosity decreases with increasing temperature, e.g., at 90°C it is about 45 per cent lower than at 60°C.

Fig. 41 shows how the densities of soap solution and oil vary with the temperatures, Fig. 42 how the viscosity of soapstock, expressed in poises, varies. The greatest reduction in viscosity occurs between 80° and 90°C, which are also the temperatures at which the difference in densities is most pronounced. These are therefore the most favourable temperatures for settling soapstock to obtain maximum recovery of neutral oil. Where good refining techniques have been applied, there is only a comparatively small proportion of neutral oil recoverable in this way, but soapstock often retains 30–40 per cent of neutral oil, calculated on the total fatty matter in the soapstock.

For efficient and rapid separation of neutral oil from soapstock high-speed centrifugal separators are now widely employed. While the speed of separation also in this case increases with temperature, with difference in densities

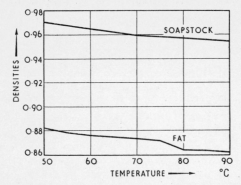

Fig. 41.   Variations in densities of soapstock and fat with temperature.

of the two materials and with the radius of the droplets, it is the centrifugal force instead of gravity which actuates the separation, and as the former can by the speed of rotation and the design of the centrifuge be increased to thousands of times that of gravity, these machines have proved highly suitable for recovery of oil from soapstock. It has also been shown in this process that dilution of the soapstock with water and increasing to some extent the pro-

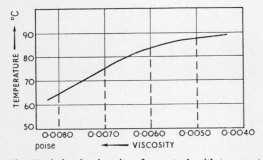

Fig. 42.   Variation in viscosity of soapstock with temperature.

portion of neutral oil lead to a more efficient separation. Some tests on De Laval soapstock centrifuges[31] have shown a recovery of 70 per cent of the neutral oil from a soapstock of 20 per cent total fatty matter, and as much as 97 per cent from a soapstock containing 64 per cent neutral oil and 4·6 per cent soap fatty matter. This high recovery of neutral oil from mixtures containing comparatively small proportions of soap has been taken advantage of in the earlier described centrifugal continuous methods of neutralizing.

When de-oiling soapstock in centrifuges the total fatty matter concentration in the soapstock is usually reduced to about 25 per cent by dilution with hot water or with a salt solution of about 15°Bé and held at a temperature of 80–85°C. Centrifuges marketed by the *De Laval Company* for this purpose range in capacity from 300–3,000 litres per hour and permit a recovery of 70–90 per cent of the neutral oil from the soapstock.

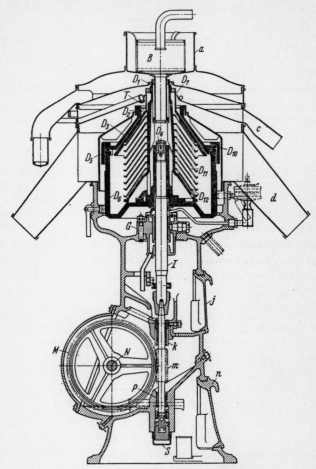

Fig. 43.   De Laval soapstock-oil separator.

Fig. 43 shows in section a De Laval soapstock separator. *j* and *n* are the cast-iron frame in which a bowl *D6*, carried by a vertical spindle *I*, revolves, supported by bearings *G*, *k* and *P*, giving perfect flexibility and absorbing all vibrations. The bowl spindle is driven from a horizontal shaft *N* by a worm gear *M*. The bowl cover *D3* is clamped on to the bowl by means of the ring *D10* with rubber packing ring *D5*, and is at the top provided with the exchangeable regulating discs *D2* with openings of different diameters in order to regulate the discharge of the heavier liquid in accordance with the density difference between that and the lighter liquid. The vertical spindle carries, in addition to the bowl, a number of conical discs; *D7* is the top disc, *D12* the lowest disc with inlet hole, *D11* a number of intermediary discs. These are all carried on the central distributor *D1*, and separated from each other by small distance pieces which leave narrow spaces for the liquid to be separated. The top disc, *D7*, has a drawn-out neck and channels on the upper side to guide the heavier liquid. Above the bowl are receptacles or covers for catching the separated liquids. The soapstock which enters through the funnel *a* via strainer *B* runs down through the central tube to the distributor below the bottom disc and is by the conical discs split up into a number of thin layers, so that the heavier liquid has only to penetrate a thin layer of fluid. The lighter liquid, oil, in the channels between the discs, passes towards the centre and up to the upper end of the neck and out through *C*. The heavier liquid, the soapstock, moves along the periphery of the bowl, up between the cover and the top disc and out through *d*, which is amply dimensioned to deal with the soap. This type of centrifuge revolves at 6000–7000 r.p.m.

As the centrifugal force acting on a particle is inversely proportional to the radius of the bowl and directly proportional to the square of the speed of rotation, and as the stress in the wall of the bowl is proportional to the speed, it will be seen that halving the radius of the bowl and doubling the speed does not alter the speed of the bowl wall and thus the stress on the wall, but doubles the centrifugal force. If, therefore, separation is difficult and only obtainable through high centrifugal force, it is advisable to reduce the bowl radius and increase the speed, even though the holding capacity of the machine is reduced. A centrifuge of this type is the Sharples Super-centrifuge shown in Fig. 44. The bowl *A* is a rather long vertical cylinder, 110 mm in diameter. It is suspended on the flexible spindle *B* from bearings *C*. The lower end runs free, but is prevented from too great deflection by guide bearing *D*. The liquid to be treated is pumped in from below under slight pressure through pipe *E*. Inside the bowl, which is 770 mm high, are three-wing baffles *F* arranged in such a way that they force the liquid to rotate with the same speed as the periphery of the bowl. The separated liquid layers move regularly from below to the top of the bowl, where the lighter oil overflows at *G* and is collected in and drained away from the cover *H* at *J*. The heavier soap solution which is adjacent to the bowl wall is flung into the other cover *L* at *K* and discharged through outlet *M*. These bowls rotate at a speed of about 15,000 r.p.m. and have a daily capacity of 2–3 tons soapstock and recover about 65 per cent of the neutral oil from the soapstock emulsion.

If soapstocks are derived from oils and fats, which have been purified by pretreatment before alkali neutralization, they are frequently used direct as raw materials in the manufacture of soap, provided they contain more than 30 per cent total fatty matter, and that their transportation is economical. Their direct use saves some alkali in the soap-making process. They can be concentrated by saponifying the neutral oil they contain and salting out the soap. If the soapstocks are derived from a process where the purification of the fat is part of the neutralization process, they can only be used direct in low-grade soaps.

In most cases, however, the soapstock is treated with mineral acid, sulphuric or hydrochloric acid, to recover and concentrate the fatty matter, which is then a mixture of fatty acids, liberated from the soap, and neutral

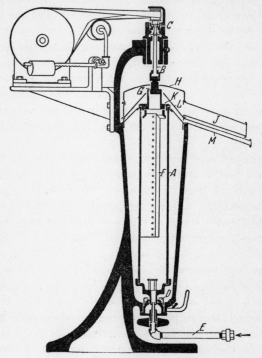

Fig. 44.   Sharples Super-centrifuge.

oil from the emulsion with soap. This mixture, often termed "acid oil", generally contains not less than 97 per cent fatty matter. The proportion of neutral oil in this mixture depends on the efficiency of the neutralization process, and from modern refineries it should not exceed 30 per cent. Acid oil is more practical to handle than soapstock, and as it usually contains less than 1 per cent water it does not incur heavy transport charges on useless material. In course of its production it can be purified and constitutes then a good material for soap making, or it can be completely hydrolyzed or "split" and the fatty acids purified by distillation.

The "splitting" of soapstock to acid oil is done in vats by adding mineral acid to the soapstock solution in such quantity that the mixture shows a slight acid reaction. Dilute hydrochloric or sulphuric acid is mostly used, although in some refineries strong sulphuric acid is preferred. The vats may be of hardwood, in which case they should be kept wet when not in use, to avoid shrinkage at the joints of the staves, or of iron or steel plated with lead to protect the iron against the acid; many refineries now use steel tanks lined with acid-resisting stoneware, set in acid-proof cement. Linings of acid-proof plastics are also coming into use; they should, however, also be alkali-proof, as the soapstock itself is alkaline. The soapstock, suitably diluted if necessary, is stirred by being boiled up with direct steam from a perforated coil, made from lead piping or other acid-resisting metal, while the acid is being added. When the soap has been decomposed and clear fatty acids and oil separate from the aqueous phase, steam is shut off and the contents of the vat left to settle. Owing to the acid vapours and the unpleasant odours, which are often caused by this treatment, the vats are usually covered and the soap-splitting section separated from the refinery.

After settling the acid waters are drained from the bottom through cocks, fittings and ducts of stainless steel, earthenware or special plastics, and the acid oil is washed free from mineral acid with hot water sprinkled on while steam is blown through. This washing is often done in separate vats. As the splitting treatment usually causes a darkening of the fatty matter, some refineries bleach the acid oil chemically or by means of bleaching earth, which is then separated by filtration in wooden filterpresses.

When analyzing acid oil for free fatty acids and neutral oil content, for the purpose of process control, consideration must be given to the molecular weight of the fatty acids concerned, as otherwise misleading results may be found.

Neutralization with Alkali Carbonate

Although caustic soda is the most frequently used alkali for neutralization, carbonate of soda is used in many cases, and particularly in recent years, since the introduction of the Clayton continuous carbonate refining process, its use has been extended to oils for which in the past it was not considered sufficiently effective.

It has the advantage that it does not attack neutral oil, and refining losses by over-saponification are therefore avoided, but its use requires a special technique to obtain good separation of the soapstock and to avoid difficulties from liberation of carbon-dioxide from the carbonate, which may lead to excessive frothing. Because of its milder action it has not the cleaning and decolorizing effect of caustic soda, as shown for instance by THURMAN[33], who found that a crude soya bean oil with a colour of 100 yellow + 9 red, as measured in the Lovibond instrument in a $5\frac{1}{4}$ in. cell, after neutralization with carbonate showed a colour reading of 100 yellow + 8 red, whereas another batch of the same crude oil after neutralization with caustic soda showed a colour of 35 yellow + 6·2 red. It is therefore often found useful to give an oil, neutralized with carbonate, a wash with weak caustic soda

71

solution—deci-normal strength—as this will improve the quality and reduce the requirements of bleaching earth in the subsequent bleaching process.

Neutralization with carbonate should be carried out at comparatively low temperature, preferably not above 50°C, so that the free fatty acids react with only one equivalent of the di-valent sodium carbonate, thus forming soap and bicarbonate:

$$R \cdot COOH + Na_2CO_3 = R \cdot COONa + NaHCO_3.$$

A large excess of carbonate is therefore mostly used, about 150 per cent excess. Development of free carbon-dioxide tends to cause froth and floating of soap particles to the surface. These must be washed to the bottom with showers of hot water, or with washes of salt or silicate.

Soda neutralization is also carried out in vacuum, thus drying the soap grains by evaporation of water and removing the free carbon-dioxide gas with the vapours. In this process the dry soap is separated from the neutralized oil by filtration.

Carbonate of soda is used both in batch operations and in continuous neutralization processes, employing centrifugal separation of the soapstock. Some examples will show different applications of the method.

In a neutralizer of the conventional type the crude material is heated to about 40°C, less if a liquid oil is being treated, and a strong carbonate of soda solution—about 35 per cent Na_2CO_3—of 40°C is added as rapidly as possible in an excess corresponding to $2\frac{1}{2}$ times the theoretical amount. By adding it rapidly sodium bi-carbonate is formed immediately and evolution of carbon dioxide avoided. The contents are stirred rapidly while the carbonate is being added, and immediately afterwards the temperature is raised by indirect steam heating till the "break" occurs; this is normally at 70–75°C, but some oils may require heating to higher temperatures. The agitation is then stopped and 50–100 per cent hot water—95°C—quickly sprayed on the oil, after which the contents are left for 1–2 hours for the soap solution to settle at the bottom. Emulsion is rarely formed and the soap solution is easily drained off; usually the neutral oil content of the soapstock is less than 30 per cent of the total fatty matter. With crude oils of inferior quality it is customary, after neutralization and removal of soapstock to give a wash with 10 per cent of a deci-normal caustic soda solution, or with a solution containing in addition to the caustic about 10 per cent salt.

To ensure that there is always a considerable excess of carbonate of soda during neutralization, and also that carbonate does not crystallize out from the strong solution, some refiners prefer to run the solution of carbonate into the neutralizing vessel first, warm it to about 45°C and add the crude oil, under vigorous stirring, at the bottom of the vessel so that it rises through the carbonate solution. After neutralization the contents are heated till the "break" takes place at about 80°C, and after stirring has been stopped a large volume of hot water is sprayed on as fast as possible to bring the soap to the bottom for settling and draining. This method is particularly effective on poor-grade oils with 6 per cent f.f.a. or more, but owing to the large amount of soap formed it is necessary to use 80–100 per cent hot water in the first wash. With better crude oil less water is required. It may at times be difficult in the carbonate of soda neutralization process to reduce the free fatty acid content below 0·1–0·15 per cent. In such cases, after the soap-stock has been drained off, the oil is given a wash with 10 per cent of a deci-normal caustic soda lye, and finally one or two washes with hot water.

DRESSLER[34] describes a method of using carbonate of soda for refining of tallow, which can also be applied to many other types of oils and fats. He recommends the use of a solution of soda ash of 25–30°Bé together with a sodium silicate solution, the two being mixed and added to the crude fat at the lowest possible temperature under stirring. The contents of the vessel are then heated to 60°C, and after stirring for a further 10–15 min. 5–7 per cent hot water is added and the fat left for settling.

The method of neutralizing with carbonate in vacuum, to which reference has been made, is carried out in different ways, one of which is as follows:

The crude oil is de-gummed and, if the soapstock is to be used for white soap, bleached before neutralization. The oil is then heated at atmospheric pressure to 35–40°C and a soda ash solution of 20 per cent strength, and in 5 per cent excess added in 10–15 min. while stirring at 65–75 r.p.m. Some evolution of carbon dioxide takes place and care must be taken to avoid excessive frothing; it is useful to have some radial arms on the agitators above the level of the liquid to destroy foam. After some minutes agitation is reduced to 15–20 r.p.m. and the pressure gradually reduced. This causes evaporation of water and release of dissolved carbon dioxide, but if the pressure reduction is gradual, for instance in course of 20–30 min., excessive frothing is avoided. To prevent cooling of the mixture by the evaporation of water indirect steam heating is applied while stirring slowly, and the temperature is maintained at about 50°C to enable the soap grains to develop and dry in the form of small flakes suitable for subsequent filtration. The length of time the oil is kept under vacuum depends on the original amount of free fatty acids, but generally 1–2 hours will ensure dryness of the soap, if the pressure is gradually reduced to about 20 mm, which corresponds to a temperature of 52°C. The soap is removed by filtration through filter-presses, often by gravity, double cloths being used in the press. A second filtration, in which a filter aid is used, is often found necessary. The soap contains about 85 per cent total fatty matter, of which about 55 per cent are soap fatty acids. The free fatty acids in the neutralized oil is usually about 0·05 per cent. The advantage of this method is that the soap by-product is dry, concentrated and easy to transport; it can be used direct for the manu-facture of good-grade soaps, particularly if the crude oil has been pre-bleached. No splitting plant is needed, thus mineral acid for splitting is saved, as well as alkali for soap-making. It is claimed that the oil from this process is particularly suitable, after deodorization, for salad oil, as its viscosity is better than that of oil neutralized by caustic lye. With semi-

73

drying oils, such as soya bean oil, difficulties are experienced because the soap is soft and tacky and difficult to filter.

Although carbonate neutralization theoretically has some advantages, it has often been found difficult to apply in practice, and most refiners have preferred the caustic lye method alone or in combination with other reagents. Since the successful introduction on industrial scale of the continuous centrifugal neutralization process with caustic lye the question of using similar plant with carbonate as the neutralizing reagent was considered and a continuous process developed by CLAYTON[35], in which neutralization was effected with soda ash and the treated oil was given a second refining with caustic soda. In this way the refining loss is reduced by using the milder alkali for neutralization, and the oil is cleaned and improved in colour by the subsequent treatment with caustic alkali. The whole process is continuous and automatically controlled and delivers the oil dried for bleaching.

Fig. 45 shows in diagrammatic form a Clayton–De Laval plant for the combined carbonate-caustic refining process which involves the use of three sets of centrifuges. The process is as follows: Strained crude oil at 20–25°C passes through a heat interchanger 34, where it is heated by the outgoing neutralized oil, and a steam preheater 33 to an automatic proportioning device 17, which adjusts the ratio of crude oil and soda ash solution. The strength of this solution is 15–20°Bé and usually 150 per cent excess is used. The soda ash solution is injected into the oil pipe line which leads to the so-called neutralizing mixer 4, where by means of a motor-driven agitator thorough mixing takes place while the charge is being further heated to cause the "break". The oil with the soap grains passes to a vacuum de-hydrator 6, where water and liberated carbon dioxide is removed, while the pressure is held at 15–20 mm abs. The mixture of oil and dry soap grains is now pumped to a re-hydration mixer 21, where soda ash solution is again added, but only sufficient to hydrate the soap to make it adequately fluid for centrifugal separation, but not wet enough to absorb oil. The dosing with soda ash solution is automatic through a special proportioning pump, and while re-hydration takes place the mixture is heated to about 95°C and then passes to a specially constructed high-speed centrifuge 20, where the soapstock is separated from the oil. The latter runs to a buffer or surge tank 45 and then to the heat-interchanger for the incoming oil 34, where it is cooled to about 27°C, which is the most suitable temperature for the next step. This is a re-refining with a caustic soda solution of 20°Bé. A pro-portioning device adds 1–2 per cent of this solution on the way to the re-refine mixer 23, where the temperature is raised to 80–85°C and which from the mixture passes to a secondary centrifuge 24 where a small quantity of darkish soap solution is separated, while the neutralized oil, partly decolorized, is pumped via a measuring arrangement for hot water to a water-wash mixer 28, for a final wash. The wash-water is separated in a third centrifuge 29 and the oil is passed to a vacuum dryer 31 for flash evaporation of the moisture left in the oil after centrifuging.

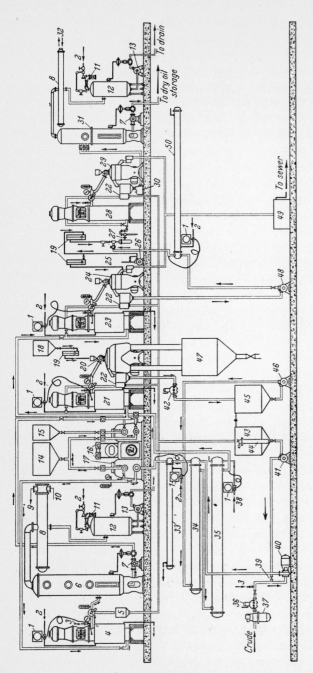

Fig. 45. Clayton-De Laval continuous carbonate neutralisation plant.

1 Temp. Controller	11 Steam ejector	21 Rehydration mixer	31 Vacuum dryer	41 Emergency pump
2 Steam	12 Receiver	22 Overflow tank	32 Cooling water	42 Flow meter "Neut Oil"
3 Air	13 Condensate pump	23 Re-refine mixer	33 Pre-heater	43 Emergency tank
4 Neutralizing mixer	14 Soda ash. 20° Bé	24 " " separator	34 Economizer	44 Level controller
5 Sample tank	15 Caustic. " "	25 Hot water pump	35 Cooler	45 Surge tank
6 Dehydrator	16 Flow meter indicators	26 " " pump	36 Flow meter "Crude Oil"	46 " pump
7 Oil Pump	17 Meter-matic pump	27 Mixing zone	37 Strainer	47 Soap tank
8 Condenser	18 Soda ash. 12° Bé	28 Water wash mixer	38 Cold water	48 Re-refine pump
9 Water outlet	19 Rotameter	29 " " separator	39 Check valves	49 Catch basin
10 Water inlet	20 Soapstock separator	30 Level control	40 Crude pump	50 Water wash heater

75

It is stated that the process works equally well on oil that has not been pre-cleaned and de-gummed. The refining losses of the combined process are lower than when caustic soda alone is used, and the oils, after the caustic wash, are as low in free fatty acids and colour as caustic-refined oils. The extra cost of the rather elaborate plant is claimed to be justified by the increased yield and the low labour cost of an automatically controlled continuous plant. MATTIKOW has summarized the practical experience with this process.[36]

NEUTRALIZATION WITH LIME AND OTHER CHEMICALS

As the alkaline earths' salts of the higher fatty acids are insoluble in water, attempts were made early to use lime or magnesia for neutralization and to separate the soaps from the neutral oil by filtration. Some refiners use caustic alkali for the main neutralization operation, and after removal of the alkali soapstock precipitate the last remnants of soap by converting it into calcium soap with calcium chloride, drying the mixture and filtering off the calcium soaps. Other refiners use slaked lime in very slight excess; a very fine emulsion is formed, as lime soap in the presence of moisture is slightly soluble in oil and acts as an emulsifier for water-in-oil dispersions. Drying the mixture in vacuum breaks the emulsion and converts the soap into a granular mass, which makes good separation by filtration possible. Separation of lime soaps is often improved by using a mixture of lime and salt. A slight variation of the lime process, which has been adopted in some refineries for neutralization of coconut oil and palm kernel oil, is carried out as follows:

The oil is warmed to about 90°C in an open vessel and dry calcium hydroxide is added, while the contents are stirred at moderate speed, about 40 r.p.m. Neutralization is generally completed in about an hour, when the mixture appears like a fine emulsion. This is now heated to about 110°C and pumped through a spray nozzle into a tall vacuum vessel, where moisture is flashed off and dry lime soaps separate from the oil. The mixture of dry soap and oil falls to the bottom of the vessel and is pumped to a filterpress for separation of the soap from the neutral oil.

Although refining losses generally are small, the alkaline earth neutralization processes have not been widely used in practice; filtration difficulties arise through slimy soaps unless the lime soaps are quite dry and in suitable granular form. Another difficulty is the disposal of the soapstock, unless it can be used direct in soapworks operating the Krebitz process.

Several other neutralizing materials have been proposed from time to time, but few have attained practical importance; sometimes they have been too expensive to justify their use for a potential minor gain in yield, sometimes they require the use of a very complicated plant. Mention should be made of ethanolamine and ammonia, which are both good neutralizing bases and can be recovered from the soapstock for repeated use. When ammonia is used the crude oil is treated at low temperature with gaseous ammonia, the soap dissolved in water, and after separation from the neutral oil the soap-stock is treated in vacuum and split into ammonia, which is re-used, and fatty acids. While it is doubtful if this method has been used industrially, several plants have operated on the K. F. WILHELM system, in which a dilute alcoholic ammonia solution is used for neutralization; the recovery of both alcohol and ammonia requires, however, a rather complicated plant.

As one of the important economic points in the neutralization process is the avoidance of loss of neutral oil, and as neutral oil can be extracted from soap by various solvents, it is not surprising that processes have been developed for carrying out the neutralization reaction in a solvent in which the neutral oil and fatty acids are soluble whereas the hydrated soaps are not. Furthermore, the solvent-oil solution is very mobile and the difference in specific gravity between solvent-oil and soap solutions is increased, hence the latter settles more easily. It has, however, been found in practice that difficulties often arise in connection with separation of the two solutions and with the economic recovery of the solvent from the soap, in which it is rather tenaciously held. P. L. FAUTH has patented a semicontinuous process, in which the oil-bearing material is extracted with solvent and the resulting miscella passed in a closed system to neutralizing vessels, where alkali is injected from the bottom into the miscella in the right proportion to neutralize the free fatty scids. A salt solution is then added to assist the separation of the soap solution, which floats to the top, as the solvent in this process—trichlorethylene —is specifically heavier than water and soap solution. The neutral oil is recovered from the miscella by evaporation of the solvent, which is re-used, and the soap solution is treated for recovery of the fatty acids.

Crude oils vary a good deal in their response to the standardized alkali neutralization processes. This may be due to variations in the quality of the oil-bearing material, such as degree of ripeness, difficulties in storage and transport, etc., differences in temperature and moisture conditions during crushing or expelling, or to the solvents used for extraction. These variations have often led refiners to try methods with other reagents, other techniques and so on, some of which have been mentioned. In nearly all cases the difficulties can be overcome more easily and economically by judicious modifications in the use of the most important neutralizing materials, namely caustic soda lye or carbonate of soda, if necessary in conjunction with salt and silicate solutions. It is therefore not surprising, that as knowledge of the nature and constituents of crude oils and fats and the changes involved in neutralization increased, the alkali neutralization processes in the various forms described, either as batch or continuous processes, have become the most important industrially.

DE-ACIDIFICATION BY DISTILLATION

To avoid the losses of neutral oil, arising from alkali neutralization of the free fatty acids, processes have been developed for removing these by distillation. Neutral oil is non-volatile, whereas fatty acids can be distilled in a current of steam in vacuum at temperatures sufficiently low to avoid pyrogenic decomposition of the oil. While HEFTER[37] already about 50 years ago pointed to the possibility of de-acidifying oil by distillation with superheated steam, several decades passed before practical methods were developed. As long as the vacuum obtainable in industrial practice was limited to one corresponding to 30–50 mm abs. pressure it was difficult, particularly in the batch distillation process, to avoid some degradation of the neutral oil, and in semi-drying oils a certain amount of polymerization as a distillation temperature of 250–290°C was required. With the development of plant for producing high vacuum, and of special alloys for stills and pipe lines to resist attack of hot fatty acids and their vapours, the process can be carried through at 3–5 mm pressure, which permits the removal of free fatty acids from a number of oils at 210–230°C. The continuous method, where the oil is heated to the high distillation temperature for only a short period, is preferable to the batch process, where the oil is exposed to the high temperature for a prolonged period, but there is even in the continuous process always the risk of polymerization in semi-drying and more unsaturated oils, in whale and fish oils. As a matter of fact, some of the plants suitable for de-acidification can be and are used for polymerization of oils.

It is important that the crude oil is purified by de-gumming before distillation as otherwise the residual neutral oil may darken at the high temperatures used. In many cases the crude oil is also pre-bleached, as some colouring matters are practically impossible to remove after the heat treatment. Pre-bleaching will also give a better colour in the distilled fatty acids, which, however, also without pre-bleaching are much superior as a by-product to those obtained by acidulation of soapstock.

The distillation de-acidification process is particularly useful on crude oils of high acidity. Whereas with crude oils of 8 per cent f.f.a. or more practical plant and process difficulties arise in alkali neutralization, the distillation process will economically deal with oils of 20–25 per cent f.f.a. As oils of such high f.f.a. content frequently contain a high proportion of mono- and di-glycerides, from partial hydrolysis of the oil, the yield of neutral oil from the distillation process is at times higher than would be expected from the f.f.a. content of the crude oil, as some of the free fatty acids, at the temperature ruling during distillation, re-esterify with the mono- and diglycerides to form triglycerides, thus increasing the yield of the neutral oil.

In practice it has been found difficult to reduce economically the free fatty acid content of the oil below 0·1–0·2 per cent. The reduction down to 1 per cent is fairly rapid, as the rate of removal of acids is proportional to their concentration in the oil. Towards neutrality the rate slows down, and when the free acid content is about 0·1–0·2 per cent slight hydrolysis of neutral oil may take place at the same time as acids are distilled off. It is therefore usually preferred to discontinue the de-acidification by distillation at 0·5–0·8 per cent f.f.a. and finish the process by neutralization with caustic alkali.

Although the neutral glycerides are practically non-volatile under the conditions of the process, a slight loss of them is incurred by entrainment in the steam and fatty acids vapours, and the distilled and condensed fatty acids contain as a rule 5–10 per cent neutral oil.

The plant for de-acidification by distillation is more expensive than that for batch neutralization. It should preferably be made from special corrosion-resisting metals. An efficient high-vacuum system as well as separate condensing systems for fatty acids and steam should be provided, and also means for obtaining the relatively high temperatures needed for distillation. These are attained by using high-pressure boilers, circulating superheated water, hot mineral oil of special quality or, as has been the preferred method in recent years, circulating dowtherm (a mixture of diphenyl and diphenyloxide) vapour in a separate heating system. The economic possibilities of the method depend therefore largely on the better yield of neutral oil and, to a minor extent, on the better value of the by-product. While its application to high-acidity crude oils may justify the economic expectations, it is doubtful whether it can compete economically with the modern methods of alkali neutralization, by batch or by continuous processes.

If the de-acidification efficiency is expressed as the "fatty acid factor" (see p. 39), i.e., the amount of fatty matter (neutral oil plus soap fatty acids) which is found in the soapstock for each per cent free fatty acids in the crude oil, figures vary widely with type and grade of oil, but are as a rule between 1·3 and 2·5, when the alkali process is used. Thus in some refineries more neutral oil is lost than fatty acids. In the distillation process the percentage loss does not increase in direct proportion to the f.f.a. content of the crude oil, hence its economic advantage on high-acidity oils. In efficient refineries using the caustic lye process on average quality crude oils the "fatty acid factor" is, however, as a rule 1·3–1·6, and therefore leaves little scope for increased economy. Hydrogenated fats and solvent extracted oils from good seeds and beans with acidities of 1 per cent or less cannot be economically de-acidified by distillation.

An example of comparisons between yields by the distillation (Wecker process) and the caustic soda processes on olive oils of different acidities is seen in Table III.

Several plants for de-acidification by distillation have been patented and described in the literature; some of them are widely used in the fatty acid distilleries. Of plants which have been used in Europe in refineries for edible oils may be mentioned those by E. WECKER, the *Lurgi Gesellschaft für Warmetechnik* and by CRAIG and *Lever Brothers Ltd*. This refining method does not appear to have been used outside Europe.

In the original WECKER plant[38] the crude oil was preheated in a heat exchanger by the outgoing oil before entering in a continuous stream the distillation vessel, which is built as a rather long and low rectangular horizontal vessel of stainless steel with a number of cross-partitions as baffles that compel the oil to travel along an extended tortuous path in shallow

TABLE III

Acidity of Crude	Yield of Neutral Oil	
	From Caustic Lye Process	From Distillation Process
(%)	(%)	(%)
2·5	93	96
5·0	88	92
10·0	78	86
20·0	58	75
30·0	38	63

layers. Along the bottom are nozzles through which a mist of water is injected into the oil, which is preheated to about 240°C and maintained at the distillation temperature in the vessel by gas heating or other means. Superheated steam is also sprayed into the oil and this, together with the mist of water, which is instantaneously converted into steam, expands rapidly in the vessel, where in the earlier plants a low pressure of about 25 mm abs. was maintained, and the fatty acids are carried off with the vapours to the condenser. WECKER claims that the use of the fine mist of water droplets by the great expansion of volume and surface promotes the rapid removal of fatty acids from the shallow layers and reduces the temperature of distillation. From crude oils containing 5–12 per cent free fatty acids about 90 per cent of these are distilled off in comparatively short time. To avoid prolonged exposure to high temperature, with the attendant risk of damage to the oil, and the large expenditure of steam required to remove last fractions of fatty acids, it is recommended to leave 1–2 per cent of free fatty acids in the oil and remove these by neutralization with caustic lye, which process also improves the colour and thus saves bleaching earth. The distillation process itself effects an improvement in colour, provided the crude oil has been de-gummed and cleaned in a pre-treatment.

The distillate passes on to a surface condenser where the fatty acids are condensed at a higher temperature—about 100° to 125°C—than is required to condense the water vapour, which is usually condensed in a barometric condenser. The de-acidified oil is continuously withdrawn from the still and cooled by the incoming oil.

In the *Bamag Ltd.* modification of the Wecker plant, as described by WILLIAMS,[39] a higher vacuum is used, 3–5 mm abs., and it is claimed that the violent expansion of the water and steam bubbles at the very low pressure not only utilizes better the stripping power of the steam, but also cools the oil and the distillate, the latter being at 120°–150°C, thereby preventing the risk of polymerization of the oil, the yield of which is near the theoretical.

Fig. 46 shows a diagram of a Bamag-Wecker de-acidification plant, in which the crude oil, after being heated in a heat exchanger by the finished oil, passes to a de-aerating tank connected to the vacuum system and via an electrical preheater, where it is heated to process temperature, to the still, which in this plant is kept at distillation temperature by electric heating.

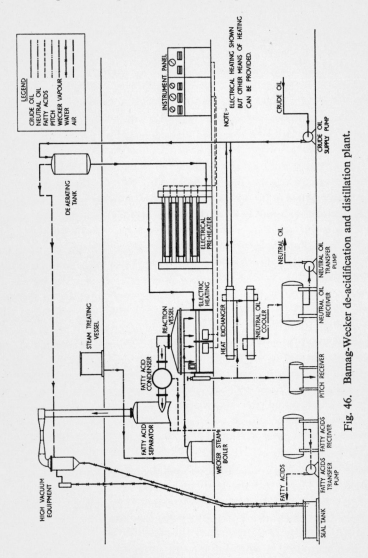

Fig. 46. Bamag-Wecker de-acidification and distillation plant.

Stripping steam is supplied by a special boiler, and the high vacuum equipment delivers the water vapours to a barometric injection condenser after the fatty acids have been condensed in the separate surface condenser.

The Lurgi de-acidification plant is similar in construction to the company's fatty acid distillation plant, and at the low pressure of about 5 mm the free fatty acids are removed at 200–210°C with little risk of damage to the oil. In a vertical cylindrical still of a special corrosion-resisting alloy superheated steam is blown through the preheated crude oil, which is kept at de-acidification temperature by a special heating system, either circulating oil or superheated water. The vapours of steam and fatty acids pass to a surface condenser, where a temperature is maintained by hot water or oil, low enough to condense the fatty acids, but not the water vapour. The condensed fatty acids are collected in a receiver, while the steam is taken by a jet booster for augmenting the vacuum to a second, barometric jet condenser where it is condensed together with the booster steam.

The method patented by R. CRAIG and *Lever Brothers Ltd.*[40] employs an oblong horizontal vessel made from a special aluminium alloy or from stainless steel, suitable for resisting fatty acid vapours. As in this process the aim is not only to distil off the free fatty acids, but also to deodorize the oil to make it suitable for edible purposes, it is essential that the crude oil is given a thorough pre-treatment, including bleaching, for which purpose an acid activated earth is recommended. The filtered bleached oil is drawn into the still, which is under high vacuum, where by means of transverse baffle-plates and an adjustable overflow pipe it is forced to follow a tortuous path in the lower half of the vessel, while steam is injected into the oil in the numerous compartments formed by the baffle plates. The lower half of the still is heated by gas to maintain the oil at a suitable temperature, which varies with the type of oil, the extent of the vacuum and the rate of removal of odoriferous compounds. At an absolute pressure of 25 mm the temperatures may be 220°–290°C. To obtain the degree of de-acidification and deodorization required for an edible oil the through-flow is rather slow, and molecular rearrangement and polymerization may take place in the oil at the comparatively high temperature. This plant is therefore, like the other distillation plants, more successfully used for de-acidification only and the free fatty acid content of the crude oil reduced to 1–2 per cent. Removal of the rest of the free acids is then effected by neutralization with caustic alkali. The oil from the still is cooled under vacuum to below 70°–80°C before coming in contact with air, and the fatty acids and steam condensed separately in the usual manner.

Fig. 47 is a diagram of a longitudinal section through the Craig plant. The pre-treated oil runs from tank *1* via pipe *2* through heat-exchanger *3*, where it is heated by the finished oil, and pipe *4* into the treatment vessel *5*, where a suitable level of oil is maintained by the adjustable overflow exit pipe *6*, which takes the finished oil through heat-exchanger *3* to cooler *7* and delivery pump. The oil is heated and kept at processing temperature by gas heating *8* or other means. Direct steam for stripping is supplied through pipe *9* and branches *10* ending in perforated distributors *11*. Baffle-plates *12* force the oil in a zigzag path through the compartments. The vessel is kept under vacuum, the vapour pipe *13* connecting with the vacuum and condensing plant.

Some other de-acidification processes by distillation are mentioned to describe the different principles employed, although the plants do not appear to have found wide application.

In the Heller process the still is under a vacuum of 20–30 mm abs. and superheated injection steam is used. If the fat predominantly consists of glycerides of C_{18} or higher-molecular fatty acids, which would require distillation temperatures of 260–290°C, a certain proportion of coconut oil with its high proportion of fatty acids of lower molecular value is added to effect a lowering of the distillation temperature. Free glycerol, arising from slight hydrolysis of coconut oil, combines with the free fatty acids of the crude fat, releasing coconut fatty acids which distil at lower temperature. In this way the distillation temperature may be reduced by 40–50°C. The Heller process is stated to reduce the f.f.a. content of the fat to 0·1 per cent. The modern high-vacuum technique, enabling a vacuum of 3–5 mm to be

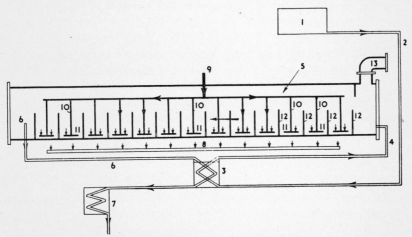

Fig. 47.   Diagram of CRAIG distillation plant.

maintained easily, would appear to make this process, with the complication of added coconut oil, superfluous.

The usual type of distillation column with plates and bubble caps has also been used for de-acidification in a current of steam, the pre-treated crude oil passing down from plate to plate in counter current against superheated steam, while a vacuum was maintained on the column. The steam carried away the free acids to the condensing and vacuum plant, and the de-acidified oil was pumped away from the bottom through a closed cooling system. Although the process gave fairly good results on such fats as coconut oil and palm kernel oil with their preponderance of C_{12} and C_{14} acids. better qualities were produced by a less complete de-acidification followed by alkali neutralization.

Removal of free fatty acids by distillation at low pressures of 15 mm or less without the use of steam has also been tried. For this purpose a stainless steel still consisting of two vertical concentric cylinders was used, the inner cylinder being heated on the inside by suitable means to the distillation temperature, while the outer cylinder was cooled on the outside to a temperature low enough to condense the fatty acids, but still keeping them fluid. The distillation of the fatty acids which in coconut oil had a boiling point, at the low pressure used, of 180–220°C took place in the annular space between the cylinder surfaces, the acids evaporating from the hot surface and being carried across the distance of about 2 cm for condensation on the cold surface. The pre-treated and de-aerated oil was supplied as a thin film to the hot surface and the de-acidified oil collected at the bottom of the hot cylindrical surface, while the fatty acids ran down in a film on the inner surface of the cooling cylinder. This method proved difficult to control, and while it operated fairly well on coconut oil down to an acidity of 0·3–0·4 per cent, the glycerides with higher-molecular fatty acids were often damaged by pyrogenic changes. In cost of operation it proved uneconomical, but it is interesting as a forerunner of the later developed methods of molecular distillation, which has found industrial application in recovery from fats of some of the minor, but valuable constituents such as vitamins, tocopherol, monoglycerides, etc. So far it has not been applied on large scale for de-acidification.

Quite recently CLAYTON[41] has patented a process in which crude oil and water, in an amount equal to 1–4 times the amount of free fatty acids, are mixed in a continuous confined stream at 200–300°C. By gradually lowering the pressure as the stream advances a mixture is formed of droplets of oil in vapours of steam and fatty acids. The stream is discharged into a vacuum evaporating chamber in not more than five minutes after mixing, which period is short enough to prevent hydrolysis of the glycerides. The vapours are withdrawn from the vacuum chamber at a rate to ensure that an absolute pressure of at least as low as 6 mm is maintained, and fatty acids and water are condensed separately while the de-acidified liquid glycerides are withdrawn from the vacuum chamber. The inventor recommends a final alkali treatment of the glycerides for removal of residual free fatty acids and some impurities not vapourized during the treatment.

There is great similarity in the principles and the methods used in steam deodorization and steam de-acidification of oils and fats, although for the former purpose temperatures usually need not be so high, and the amounts of volatile substances removed are much smaller. It is, therefore, only to be expected that the steam de-acidification process effects, at any rate on pre-treated oils, a partial deodorization, and in this manner reduces the cost of subsequent deodorization to edible standard. The patent of CRAIG and *Lever Brothers Ltd.*, as already mentioned, covers the combination of the two processes. When the ultimate use of the de-acidified fat is for high-grade edible products, it is essential that the crude material is given an adequate de-gumming and purification pre-treatment, as the relatively high processing temperature may cause decomposition of the impurities, resulting in darkening of the fat and the distilled fatty acids and in formation of malodorous compounds, some of which are soluble in and may condense with the acids and some remain in the de-acidified fat and may be difficult to remove by deodorization. The distilled fatty acids contain as a rule 5–10 per cent neutral fat, partly carried over by entrainment in the steam, partly distilled over in accordance with the partial vapour pressure of the glycerides, which however is low compared with that of the fatty acids.

While de-acidification by steam distillation normally cannot compete economically with the modern methods of alkali neutralization, it has a useful field of application on high-acidity oils and fats, which previously were not considered economically suitable for refining for edible purposes, and they have also found a use in recovery of distilled fatty acids of good quality from "acid oil" obtained by acid splitting of soapstock.

DE-ACIDIFICATION BY SOLVENT EXTRACTION

The differential solubilities of fatty acids and neutral glycerides in various organic solvents have formed the basis of several processes for de-acidification of crude oils and fats. Pyridine, for instance, has been suggested as a solvent for crude oil, as on addition of a small percentage of water the neutral glycerides will be precipitated while the fatty acids remain in solution. The solvent is recovered by distillation and re-used.

More attention has been given to alcohol as a solvent for fatty acids. These, apart from the higher-molecular ones such as stearic acid, etc., are soluble in absolute alcohol and in slightly hydrated alcohol, even in the cold. On the other hand, neutral fats, except castor oil, are very sparingly soluble in alcohol. Even stearic acid, which by itself is only very slightly soluble in cold alcohol, becomes soluble when mixed with other fatty acids.

In spite of this differential solubility of fatty acids and neutral glycerides it has not not been possible to obtain with alcohol a complete separation of the two materials, because the low solubility of the glycerides in alcohol is increased in proportion to their content of free fatty acids. The neutral glyceride acts as a solvent both for fatty acids and alcohol. Therefore, if a fat containing free fatty acids is treated with alcohol two phases are obtained, one being a solution of fatty acids and neutral fat in alcohol, the other a solution of alcohol and fatty acids in neutral fat. Quantitative separation is therefore not possible, and separation becomes increasingly difficult with increase of free acids in the crude fat. This question has been studied by TAYLOR et al.[42] who showed that neutral oil mixed with equal parts of oleic acid is completely miscible with 2 volumes of 90 per cent alcohol and with $\frac{1}{3}$ part oleic acid with absolute alcohol. As stated, the solubility increases in proportion to the free acid content until the neutral oil finally becomes completely soluble. Consequently de-acidification with alcohol can be only partially successful, and entails also a loss of neutral oil with the alcoholic solution of fatty acids. For complete de-acidification it is therefore necessary to give the alcohol-extracted oil a final neutralization treatment with alkali.

BOLLMANN[43] suggested a method employing the principle of counter current leaching of crude fat with ethyl alcohol, amyl alcohol, ethyl acetate, etc., in a series of tanks filled with packing rings, which promote intimate contact without causing strong agitation that might set up emulsions, but this method as well as the other methods for alcohol extraction of the fatty acid have, for the reasons indicated, not gained much favour.

SCHLENKER[44] claims to get better results when using for de-acidification a mixture of alcohol and glycerol, and quotes as an example the reduction in acidity of sulphur olive oil from 55 per cent f.f.a. to 14 per cent when 100 parts oil were treated with 135 parts 92·5 per cent alcohol and 65 parts glycerol. Final treatment with alkali is, however, necessary for neutralization, and the cost will, except in special circumstances, make the process uneconomical. Nothing is stated about process losses which must be high.

The patent literature shows a wide selection of methods for effecting de-acidification with solvents of various kinds, soaps, acid esters of polyvalent alcohols with the lower fatty acids (up to C_3) and the lower alkyl esters of formic acid, but they have not proved of industrial value, or only applicable in special cases. During the last decade, however, processes have been introduced, particularly in U.S.A., the so-called liquid-liquid extraction processes, which were originally and essentially intended for fractionation of glycerides or fatty acids, but have been shown to be applicable also to the separation of free fatty acids from glycerides, not as a separate process, but as part of the fractionation process. The use of the two most effective solvents for this purpose, namely furfural and propane, should therefore be briefly mentioned.

The furfural process has been developed by the *Pittsburgh Plate Glass Company*[45] to produce from semi-drying oils, for instance, soya bean oil, fractions more and less saturated than the original crude oil, but in the treatment the free fatty acids largely follow the more unsaturated fraction, called the extract, whereas the less unsaturated fraction, the raffinate, is practically free from free fatty acids. Furfural is at room temperature only partially miscible with oil, more with the unsaturated part than with the saturated, though the difference is small. However, by using a tall packed column, to which furfural is admitted near the top, the crude oil lower down near the middle, the specifically heavier furfural, moving towards the bottom in continuous counter-current against the oil, dissolves and carries to the bottom the more unsaturated fraction, while the more saturated fraction with some furfural is removed from the top. The solvent is recovered from the two fractions by distillation and re-used. Some of the extract can be admitted at the bottom of the column as a reflux, and by varying the ratio of solvent to oil, the temperature and the amount of reflux, the proportions of extract and raffinate can be varied. As the free fatty acids and impurities largely follow the extract, the process serves as a method of de-acidifying the raffinate. As an example[46] it may be mentioned that a soya bean oil with iodine value 138·1 and 0·55 per cent free fatty acids can be fractionated into 40 per cent raffinate with iodine value 117·5 and 0·018 per cent f.f.a., and 60 per cent extract with iodine value 151·5 and 0·85 per cent f.f.a. In this operation 11·1 parts furfural were used to 1 part oil with 1·56 parts reflux. The raffinate is a better material than the original oil for preparations for edible purposes, not only because of its more suitable glyceride composition and low f.f.a. content, but also because it is partially purified and decolorized, thereby facilitating subsequent bleaching and deodorizing. The inclusion of a small proportion of naphtha (145–185°C B.P.) in the reflux helps the separation of the fractions. Treatment of the extract in a second

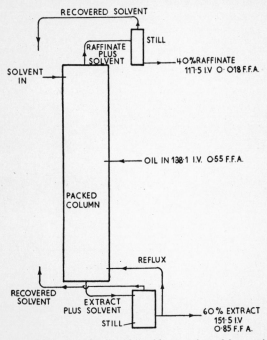

Fig. 48. Flow-sheet for liquid-liquid extraction of fatty acids.

column with a mixture of furfural and naphtha effects separation of extract from free fatty acids and impurities, yielding a practically de-acidified extract as a valuable drying oil and a small fraction, about 1 per cent of fatty acids and impurities.[47] Fig. 48 shows diagrammatically the system of operating the furfural process.

Propane is used in the liquid-liquid extraction process patented by the M. W. Kellog Co.[48, 49]. It is entirely miscible with fats and oils at lower temperatures, but near its critical temperature (97°C) it is only partially miscible, the saturated constituents being more soluble than the unsaturated. As propane is a gas at atmospheric pressure—it boils at − 44°C—the process is carried out under a pressure of several hundred pounds, and as it is specifically lighter than oil it moves in counter current towards the top of the column, leaving the extract at the bottom, and refluxes from the top. Being a non-polar solvent propane is less selective for fractionation of the glycerides than is furfural, but it is particularly effective for removing impurities present in minor proportions such as free fatty acids, phosphatides, sterols, colouring matters, etc., and can be used for concentration and extraction of valuable minor constituents such as vitamins from fish liver oils. The process has already found industrial application for removing coluring matters and other impurities from tallow, but as a de-acidification process *per se* it is hardly likely to be economically competitive.

De-acidification by Esterification

To re-combine with fresh glycerol the free fatty acids, which owe their presence in crude fats, to hydrolysis with loss of glycerol at an earlier stage, would appear to be the rational method of de-acidification and, at the same time, of increasing the supply of fat. Where, however, the free fatty acid content of the crude fats and oils is of the normal order, i.e., less than 6–7 per cent, the process of re-combination, esterification, is not economical. In practice it is difficult to reduce the acidity below 1 per cent, and consequently it is necessary to follow esterification by an alkali neutralization. The price of glycerine and the price differences between neutral fat and fatty acids are generally such that the process is uneconomical. Where, however, the difference between the edible fat and the acids is high, as, for instance, with olive oil, Borneo tallow and a few others, it pays in many cases to esterify crude fats with 7–8 per cent f.f.a. or more, and similarly under conditions of restricted war economy. The process has therefore found its principal application on high-acid olive oil in Mediterranean countries and on acid oils and fatty acids in Central European countries, for example, the acid oils obtained by acidulation of soapstock from alkali neutralization which may contain from 30–80 per cent free fatty acids.

While the process of esterifying fatty acids with glycerol leads to practically complete formation of triglycerides, it is not yet sufficiently under control to ensure the combination of the acids with glycerol in the same pattern of distribution in the molecule as in the original fat before hydrolysis. In many cases this may not be a detriment, as in recent years improvements in the physical characteristics of natural fats have often been effected by a change in the molecular arrangement by the inter-esterification process. Esterification may therefore lead to a new fat rather different from the original one. This applies to a much greater extent when the alcohol for esterification is other than glycerol, for instance, ethyl alcohol, which in several periods has been employed on a large industrial scale on the Continent in the manufacture of so-called ester-oils.

Glycerol reacts with fatty acids at fairly high temperatures, 250–300°C, in vacuum—even without the use of catalysts—to form triglycerides, but the reaction is too slow and incomplete to be of practical value, particularly if the reactants are present in dilution of a large proportion of neutral glycerides. In the presence of a suitable catalyst, however, the reaction is much more rapid and can be carried out in high vacuum—to remove immediately the water formed—at such lower temperatures, 150–225°C, that industrial application is possible without excessive degradation and discoloration of the fat. Of the many different catalysts tried, mostly metal oxides and salts, the most effective have been those of tin and zinc—$SnCl_4$, $SnCl_2$, $ZnCl_2$—used in the proportion of 0·1–0·2 per cent, calculated on the metal content. Used at temperatures of 175–200°C and at an absolute pressure of 10–30 mm the reaction proceeds towards neutrality in a few hours. In practice it is rarely taken below 2 per cent f.f.a., as the reaction slows down considerably towards the end, and the esterified fat is given an alkali treatment afterwards in any case to remove the catalyst. The reaction is rather complex and there is evidence that it proceeds via formation of a metal salt of the fatty acid, free hydrochloric acid and chlorohydrin to glyceride and metal chloride.[50]

The first recorded industrial use of esterification of acid oils and fatty acids was during the 1914–1918 war when SCHLINCK in Germany took out a patent[51] which, because of the high price and shortage of glycerine and the high temperature and process difficulties under the then existing conditions, recommended the use of other alcohols than glycerine for esterification and specifically covered the use of ethylene glycol. With modern plants, built of special stainless steel, provided with stirrers for efficient contact between the reactants and equipped with condensers for refluxing glycerol as well as high-vacuum devices to keep the reaction temperature as low as 150–180°C, the technical difficulties are overcome and the application of the process is essentially an economic question.

Esterification of distilled fatty acids with natural or synthetic glycerol was done on a large scale in Germany during the last war. The fatty acids were obtained by oxidation of synthetic or natural hydrocarbons or by hydrolysis and distillation of soapstock acids. Stainless steel plant with water-cooled reflux condensers packed with Raschig rings was used and zinc dust employed as catalyst. The process took about 8 hours to reduce the free fatty acids to 0·7 per cent and the reaction which started at 120°C was carried through at increasing temperatures up to 180°C. It was necessary to give the resulting product an alkali neutralization before passing it on for further treatment for edible use.

When glycerine has been costly or difficult to obtain other alcohols have been used for esterification, and in addition to the earlier mentioned process employing glycol, which has not been accepted everywhere as physiologically unobjectionable, methods were developed for esterification of distilled fatty acids and acid oils with ethyl alcohol. The industrial use of this process is definitely a wartime feature, and took place in Germany both during the 1914–1918 war and the recent one. The process is easily carried out by mixing in a stainless steel vessel, provided with condenser, the fatty material with

89

7

the appropriate amount of ethyl alcohol—for distilled acids 18 per cent alcohol is used—and using 5 per cent of strong sulphuric acid as condensing agent for the reaction. Owing to the low boiling-point of alcohol the process takes place at 80°C and in vacuum and is usually completed in 4–5 hours, according to the percentage of free fatty acids present. After completion of the reaction the sulphuric acid is drained off and excess alcohol removed by distillation. Also in this process the de-acidification is completed by washing the product with a caustic soda solution, before it is treated further for edible purposes.

As ethyl alcohol is a monohydric alcohol the product of the esterification is a mixture of ethyl esters of monovalent fatty acids and has not the complex composition of the true fats from mixed glycerides. No physiological objection has been raised to their use as foods, but their use in edible products, such as margarine, has been criticized on account of quality. They are apt to hydrolyse in the deodorization process, which therefore must be carried through at a much lower temperature (120–130°C) than with natural fats, and preferably in a mixture with equal proportions of natural fat; consequently it is difficult to make the product quite free from odour. There is also in margarine made from it a tendency to hydrolysis with the development of ester-like odours. These so-called esteroils are softer and of poorer consistency than the corresponding glycerides, and the use of more than 10 per cent in the margarine fat-blend was rarely attempted.

While de-acidification by esterification is an interesting technical development, it can only in exceptional and special cases be considered of industrial importance as a means of increasing the supply of fats for edible purposes. More important industrially is the esterification of distilled fatty acids and the related process of inter-esterfication of glycerides.

III. Bleaching or Decoloration

AN important step in refining is the removal of undesirable colouring matters; it is generally referred to as *bleaching* or *decoloration*. As already mentioned under *neutralization*, some colouring matters are usually removed in that process, particularly when strong alkali solutions are used, but some are strongly fat-soluble and are natural and characteristic constituents of the crude fats and oils; they cannot be looked upon as impurities and can only be removed by special treatment.

The natural colouring matters are principally carotene, xanthophyll and chlorophyll. Others, less well defined, may also be present. They are derived from the oil-bearing materials or, in the case of some animal fats, from the fodder of the animals, and they give the crude fats and oils their characteristic yellow, orange or greenish shades.

Other colouring matters found in the crude oils may be degradation products of the natural colours, or may be the result of the processing of the oil-bearing material, unsuitable storage, oxidation, etc. Oilseed stored for prolonged periods under unfavourable temperature and moisture conditions and exposed to air oxidation yield darker coloured fats than fresh seed, partly due to deterioration of the fat itself, such as by formation of oxy-fatty acids, partly due to a browning-reaction between protein and carbohydrate in the gums and mucilage. These colours are difficult to bleach. Dark colour may also be caused by high cooking temperature in hydraulic pressing and expelling of oil seed, partly by oxidation of the oil, partly by colour bodies extracted by the hot oil from the seed and seed coat. Therefore oils from second pressings at higher pressures and temperatures are always darker than those from first pressings. In the solvent extraction process lighter coloured fats are extracted with petroleum spirit—benzine—than when trichlorethylene, benzol or some other solvents are used which are less selective towards the fat.

Animal fats, which when fresh are white or pale yellow, may be darkened by decomposition products from the adipose tissues as the result of too high rendering temperature or local overheating during the process.

Darkening of oils may also to some extent be due to oxidation of one of the unsaponifiable constituents, γ-tocopherol, itself colourless, but when oxidized to chroman-5, 6-quinone giving a brownish colour to the oil[52].

Colour reduction in the fat may be effected in the several steps of the complete refining process as follows:

1. By neutralization with caustic lye. The soapstock carries down a proportion of the colouring matter, partly by a mechanical process, partly by coagulation and interaction between the electro-negative soap particles and electro-positive colour colloids. Colouring matters formed by gums, proteins, etc., may also be flocculated with the soapstock.

2. If the crude fat is submitted to a pre-treatment before neutralization, some of the colour may be removed by the action of one of the reagents used, for instance, tannin, sulphuric acid, salt, etc. The most effective is concentrated sulphuric acid. THURMAN found[53] that a soya bean oil, having a colour of 100 Yellow plus 9 Red on the Lovibond scale ($5\frac{1}{4}$ in.) after treatment with concentrated sulphuric acid showed a colour of 35 Yellow plus 4 Red.

3. After the pre-treatment and the neutralization with caustic there are still present in many oils and fats some colouring compounds, probably largely of different chemical composition from those removed with the alkali, particularly carotenoids and chlorophylls, and it is therefore often necessary to give the neutral fat a further bleaching, in accordance with the purpose for which the fat is intended. Generally speaking, most of the colouring matters, which are due to deterioration, are removed by pre-treatment and neutralization, hence the efficiency of

these facilitates subsequent bleaching; there are, however, some degradation products which give a very tenacious colour, difficult to remove; these together with the natural colouring matters require the application of special bleaching processes.

The extent to which a fat should be bleached is entirely a question of its future use. Most salad oils and oils for mayonnaise are required of a bright yellow or yellowish-green colour. High-grade olive oils have this colour, and inferior oils, which have been refined and bleached to remove brownish and dark colours caused by deterioration, often have to be artificially coloured to resemble in colour the better grades. While the natural colouring matters are on the whole unobjectionable as regards their effect on flavour, the deterioration colours are frequently associated with undesirable flavours and their removal by bleaching improves the flavour of the product. Many fats and oils for edible purposes, for example, for salad oils and margarine, are therefore only bleached to remove deterioration colours and excess of natural colouring matter, which might interfere with final artificial coloration to the desired shade. Certain fats, such as coconut oil, palm kernel oil, lard, etc., are in their pure state white and are therefore, when refined, bleached to a white colour. The same applies to hydrogenated and other fats required for the manufacture of certain types of shortenings and lard substitutes. Often a white colour is taken to connote purity and high quality, but there is in many cases no justification for this. In palm oil, for example, some of its high carotene content is frequently deliberately retained, because it confers valuable properties on the fat for certain edible purposes.

It is not only for edible use that fat is bleached; for the manufacture of white soaps it is also necessary to use thoroughly bleached fats, and drying oils used in the production of white and light-coloured paints should also as far as possible be colourless.

Bleaching is carried out in various ways:

A. The most important method in industry is decoloration by adsorption, in which materials with high surface activity, such as bleaching earths or bleaching carbons, retain the colouring substances by adsorption, while having no effect on the fat itself.

B. Bleaching of the fat by chemical action by which the colouring substances are destroyed by oxidation or changed into colourless compounds.

C. Hydrogenation in the presence of various catalysts has a strong bleaching effect, particularly on carotenoids. The orange-yellow colour of palm oil, which is due to several carotenes, can be entirely discharged by hydrogenation, and if this process is carried out under special conditions, bleaching can be completed without significant hydrogenation of the glycerides.

D. The process referred to under de-acidification as liquid-liquid extraction of fatty acids can be adjusted to operate for extracting a fraction containing colouring matters and other impurities, and propane is now used on industrial scale for bleaching tallow.

92

E. Bleaching by heat is effective on carotenoids, and is used on large scale in combination with adsorption bleaching and in course of the deodorization process. On the other hand, some colouring matters, not removed in the adsorption bleach, may cause darkening of the fat when exposed to the high deodorization temperature.

The chemical method of bleaching has, since the introduction of the modern activated bleaching earths and carbons, become comparatively unimportant, and is practically never used on fats and oils intended for edible purposes. Oxidation bleaching by air is still finding application on technical palm oil and tallows, fatty acids and low-grade oil otherwise difficult to bleach, but as it is impossible by this method to avoid some oxidation of the glyceride as well, the fat is only treated by this process if a slight discoloration in the final product is unimportant.

The advantage of carrying out the bleaching on the fats after pre-treatment and neutralization has already been pointed out. There are, however, frequently cases when bleaching is done on the crude fats with or without pre-treatment, as for instance, when the acid oil or soapstock from the neutralization process is wanted of pale colour or white.

Adsorption Bleaching

The adsorbents used for bleaching fats and oils are predominantly natural and acid-activated clays, hydrated aluminium silicates, and to a lesser extent activated carbons. They possess the power to adsorb on their surface not only the colour compounds, but also other in oil colloidally suspended substances such as gums, resins and certain degradation products. Whether the adsorption of the colouring matter is a pure physical phenomenon is not quite clear. At the surface of the adsorbent some of the valences, which hold the atoms together, are free, and LANGMUIR has suggested formulae for adsorption based on forces operating in a manner similar to those in chemical reactions. Chemisorption with bleaching clays could be explained by the formation of salts between the colour compounds and the reactive hydrogen and aluminium ions in the aluminium-hydrosilicates. Bleaching with carbons appears to be a pure physical phenomenon. In both cases, however, the course of decoloration is analogous and follows largely the laws of adsorption.

In the range of concentration of the solute—the material to be removed by adsorption—and the temperatures normally occurring in bleaching of fats the relationship between the amount of solute adsorbed and the final concentration follows the VAN BEMMELEN-FREUNDLICH equation for the adsorption isotherm,[54]

$$\frac{x}{m} = a \, C^{1/n}.$$

In this equation x is the amount of solute adsorbed by m grammes of adsorbent, C is the concentration of solute in the solution, a and $1/n$ are the adsorption constants of which *a* represents the adsorption value of the adsorbent material or the adsorption at unit concentration; it is characteristic of the adsorbent and the solute adsorbed. $1/n$ is the adsorption exponent indicating the quality or efficiency of the adsorption at varying concentrations of the solute. The higher *a* and the smaller $1/n$, the more valuable the adsorbent.

If x/m is plotted against C, curves of the general parabolic type are obtained. Fig. 49 shows two such curves, *A* and *B*, similar in type, but representing two different oils on different adsorbents. This equation expresses the charac-

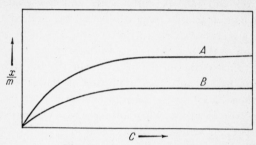

Fig. 49.   Adsorption curves.

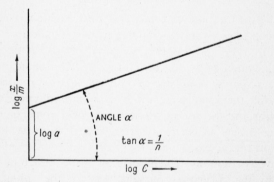

Fig. 50.   FREUNDLICH'S adsorption isotherm, log.-log. scale.

teristic that the amount of solute adsorbed per unit weight of adsorbent is proportional to the concentration of solute in the solution until an equilibrium is reached.

The equation can also be written in the logarithmic form,

$$\log x/m = \log a + 1/n \log C.$$

This expression is linear, and the graph obtained by plotting $\log x/m$ against $\log C$ is a straight line which intercepts the $\log x/m$ axis at a height representing $\log a$; the slope gives an angle with the $\log C$ axis, whose tangent is $1/n$. Fig. 50 shows a graph of this type.

The values of *a* and $1/n$ can be determined experimentally on each adsorbent by plotting colour reduction per unit adsorbent against residual colour on a logarithmic scale graph. x/m and C may be expressed in any convenient units and the numerical value of a depends on these. For instance, the measurement of colour and colour reduction may be assessed in additive units of Lovibond standard glasses or by standardized colour comparators, such as dichromate solutions.

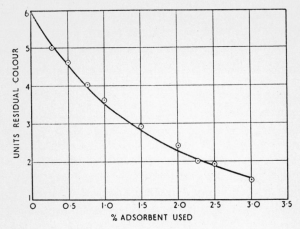

Fig. 51.   Colour reduction curve.

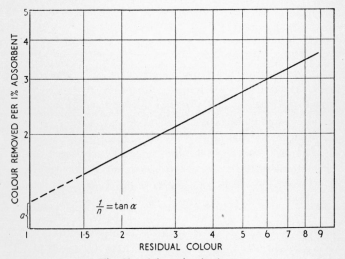

Fig. 52.   Adsorption isotherm.

Table IV shows an example of colour units adsorbed (x), residual colour (C), and colour units adsorbed per unit adsorbent (x/m), when an oil of original colour of 6 units is bleached with different percentages of adsorbent. Fig. 51 shows the graph when residual colour is plotted against percentage of adsorbent used. Fig. 52 is the adsorption isotherm on logarithmic scale.

95

TABLE IV. Bleaching test on oil, original colour 6 units

% Adsorbent Used (m)	Colour Units Adsorbed (x)	Residual Colour Units (C)	Units Adsorbed per Unit Adsorbent (x/m)
0·5	1·3	4·7	2·85
1·0	2·3	3·7	2·3
1·5	3·1	2·9	2·05
2·0	3·6	2·4	1·8
2·5	4·15	1·85	1·66
3·0	4·5	1·5	1·5

The amount of solute—colour and colloids—removed per unit weight of adsorbent is, as stated earlier, proportional to the concentration of the solute; as concentration decreases there is a progressive decrease in solute removed, until an equilibrium is reached and with a particular fat further removal is insignificant. If this stage is reached before the adsorbent is saturated, it can still be used for removing some of the colouring matter from a stronger coloured fat. This indicates that a counter-current system of bleaching might be effective, but other factors, such as the very fine particle size of some of the adsorbents, the possibility of adsorbed oxidized fat catalyzing fresh supplies, and other solutes than colouring matter and colloids being present, introduce practical difficulties, which, however, seem to have been overcome in some semi-counter-current systems. As will be described later, adsorption bleaching on fats and oils is generally by the batch system and rarely on fixed adsorption beds.

The values of a and $1/n$ vary with the fats and the adsorbents, and often with different consignments of the same fat and adsorbent. a is proportional to the active surface of the adsorbent. The capillaries in the interior of the particles of the adsorbent are, however, generally ineffective, as the solutes are mostly high-molecular and often colloidal and impede diffusion. Equilibrium on the surface is therefore reached before the full adsorption capacity is utilized, and the practical adsorption value is consequently not dependent on the total capillary surfaces, but on that of the particles or grains; hence when bleaching fats and oils the finer the grain-size, the higher the bleaching capacity and rate per unit weight of adsorbent. This is confirmed by practical experience. The refiner, by the pretreatment, endeavours to eliminate the variations from the fat, and the manufacturer of the bleaching adsorbents works very closely to standard grades, but sometimes their transport and storage may introduce slight irregularities.

There are some records in literature of tests to determine a and $1/n$. BAILEY[55] gives for good activated earth and neutralized cottonseed oil a about 1·0–1·2 and $1/n$ about 0·8. HASSLER and HAGBERG[56] describe experiments with fuller's earth, activated carbon and mixtures of the two in the ratio 10:1 on cottonseed oil, and find a and $1/n$ values in the three cases of 0·6 and 0·45, 0·2 and 2·2, and 0·76 and 0·6 respectively.

In practice the selection and evaluation of bleaching earths and carbons is generally guided by laboratory tests, devised to simulate the varying conditions of materials and types of plant and to predict the results which may be obtained on full factory scale. Apart from decoloration efficiency, other points to consider in selecting adsorbents are oil retention, rate of filtration, and the effect of filtration on quality. These points will be dealt with in a later chapter.

Bleaching Earths

1. *Source and Effect*.—Towards the end of the nineteenth century deposits were discovered in England (Surrey, Kent, Somerset, Bedfordshire) and America (Florida, Arkansas, Virginia, Texas) of special non-plastic clays which were found unsuitable for ceramics, but had the power to remove colour bodies from mineral oils and from fats. The clay from English sources, which had already found use for "fulling" in the textile industry, was called "fuller's earth"—the American product Floridin, from its place of origin. Since then several deposits of bleaching clays have been found in other countries, Czechoslovakia, Rumania, Japan, India and in Russia, where extensive deposits are known as Gluchower Kaolin. The general description "bleaching earths" or "bleaching clays" is now used, and defines clays which after suitable cleaning and grinding possess the power to decolorize fats and oils.

In addition to those which in their natural state have decolorizing properties there are some clays which are either inactive or very weak decolorizers, but which after treatment with mineral acids, generally sulphuric or hydrochloric acid, exhibit much enhanced bleaching power. They are called "activated clays" or "activated bleaching earth" (in Germany, Edelerden) in contradistinction to the "natural" bleaching earths.

The glycerides themselves are normally not changed by the treatment with bleaching earths, although the more highly unsaturated glycerides, when heated in the presence of air, can undergo some oxidation as the result of some catalytic action of the earth. Bleaching, particularly at elevated temperature, should therefore preferably be done in closed vessels and under vacuum, when a change in the glycerides as an effect by bleaching earth or activated carbon does not occur. BENEDICT[57] noticed that the activity of the bleaching earths corresponded to their power to oxidize MOHR's salt (ferrous ammonium sulphate), but could not demonstrate that the oxidation of the ferrous salt did not result from the catalytic effect of the bleaching earth. If the latter had been treated with hydrogen it failed to reduce MOHR's salt, and as the hydrogen treatment could not cause any drastic change in the chemical composition of the earth there was no proof in his findings. It was also admitted that no oxidation changes were noticed in the oils, and that generally the course of decoloration followed FREUNDLICH's adsorption isotherm, which would not be the case with an oxidizing agent.

The slight deviation from the adsorption isothern sometimes shown in bleaching with adsorbents can be explained by the presence in the oil of several solutes, such as different groups of colouring matters with varying affinities for the adsorbent, in some cases even not adsorbed on the particular earth. Furthermore, there may also be present colourless solutes, colloids and traces of soap which are adsorbed from the oil.

The amount and kind of bleaching earth or carbon required to decolorize the fat depends on the type and colour of the latter and on the extent of decoloration desired. The average proportion of adsorbent is usually 1·5–2·5 per cent with good activated earth. The bleaching materials absorb considerable quantities of the fatty solvent, particularly when very fine-grained material of high bleaching power is used, and although much of this fat can be recovered by various processes, it is of darker colour and less valuable than the original unbleached material. This loss of fat, or its degradation as a by-product in the bleaching process, forms a considerable proportion of the total refining cost.

2. *Composition. Difference between Decoloring and Non-decoloring Clays. Activation.*—The bleaching earths are silicates of different compositions, the main constituents being SiO_2 and Al_2O_3; they contain chemically bound water. In addition, calcium, magnesium and iron oxides, etc., are found, which however do not appear to contribute to the bleaching power.

The percentage composition of the clays affords no guide as to their bleaching capacity, nor is the suitability of a clay for activation by mineral acid ascertainable by analysis. Ceramic kaolin shows often similar chemical composition to fuller's earth.

According to DECKERT[58] the inactive raw clay from Landau (Bavaria) has similar composition to the naturally active American Florida earth:

TABLE V

	Landau Raw Earth (%)	Florida Earth (%)
SiO_2	59	56·53
Al_2O_3	22·9	11·57
Fe_2O_3	3·4	3·32
CaO	0·9	3·06
MgO	1·2	6·29

The Landau earth can by treatment with mineral acid be changed into a highly active bleaching earth, whereas the activity of the Florida earth cannot be increased.

Table VI shows analyses of three naturally active American bleaching earths (*A*, *B*, and *D*) and an inactive type of kaolin (*C*)[59]:

TABLE VI

	A (%)	B (%)	D (%)	C (%)
SiO_2	72·95	58·10	57·95	58·72
Al_2O_3	12·65	15·43	0·85	16·01
Fe_2O_3	3·56	4·95	—	2·12
FeO	0·47	0·3	—	—
MgO	0·57	2·44	19·71	3·3
CaO	1·0	1·75	4·17	1·05
Na_2O	0·2	0·27	1·84	2·11
K_2O	0·68	0·66	0·43	1·50
CO_2	—	0·84	1·22	—

DAVIS and MESSER, who recorded these analyses, believe that there is a difference in the $SiO_2:Al_2O_3$ ratio of inactive and active or activatable clays. This ratio is highest in the natural bleaching earths and lowest in the inactive clays. In the activatable clays this ratio would be higher than in the ceramic clays, but not as high as in the natural bleaching earths. Treatment with mineral acid raises this ratio of $SiO_2:Al_2O_3$ from the original 2–3:1 to 5–6:1, as shown in the comparison below (Table VII) of the analyses of an activatable clay before and after activation.

TABLE VII

	Before Activation (%)	After Activation (%)
SiO_2	47·38	59·3
Al_2O_3	15·38	9·53
Fe_2O_3	3·57	1·7
MgO	4·24	3·2
CaO	2·25	1·13

The view, that the ratio $SiO_2:Al_2O_3$ should be characteristic for active and activatable clays, is of doubtful accuracy; thus Russian natural active kaolins are very rich in Al_2O_3; Gluchow kaolin with high bleaching power contains, according to LJALIN and WARISINA[60], 33·1 per cent Al_2O_3 to 50·4 per cent SiO_2. This clay has approximately the same bleaching power as Floridin with only 11·57 per cent Al_2O_3 to 56·53 per cent Si_2O_3. It seems therefore futile to relate composition to the bleaching activity of clays.

According to DAVIS and MESSER[59], good natural bleaching earths are distinguished by the absence of water-soluble salts and often by high hydrolytic acidity. Most English fuller's earths need for neutralization of the aqueous extract from 100 g clay 10–150 cc N/10 NaOH. The Japanese Kambara clay also gives an acid aqueous extract. This clay contains, according to UENO[61], 70·1–63 per cent SiO_2, about 15 per cent Al_2O_3 and 2·3–4·5 per cent Fe_2O_3, which is a similar composition to that of American and English natural bleaching earths and the Bavarian activatable raw clay, and like the other bleaching clays it is an amorphous, slightly plastic material. The hydrolytic acidity is not characteristic of the natural bleaching clays of California and Nevada; the aqueous extract from 100 g of these clays has an alkaline reaction and requires 5–100 cc N/10 HCl. for neutralization. Several American clays activatable by means of mineral acid also give alkaline aqueous extracts. It is therefore clear that hydrolytic acidity is as useless for recognizing bleaching clays as the percentage composition.

More elucidation has been obtained in recent years by studying the mineralogy and chemical structure of the bleaching clays, their behaviour on heating, etc.

KERR[62] found the mineral montmorillonite to be the principal constituent in fuller's earth and bleaching bentonite. This has been confirmed by HOFMANN, ENDELL and WILM[63]. Of a large number of fuller's earths and bleaching clays which have been studied, 54 contained as chief constituent a clay mineral of the montmorillonite type $H_2O \cdot 4SiO_2 \cdot Al_2O_3 \cdot nH_2O$, apart from the usual admixtures of quartz, etc. It showed the characteristic phenomenon of one-dimensional swelling with polar liquids (water). DAVIS and MESSER had already suggested that the swelling-power in water is a characteristic property of all activatable clays, but from this the reverse conclusion should not be drawn, that because a clay shows swelling-properties, it can be activated. Of two examined specimens of bentonite with equal swelling power one could be effectively activated, the other not.

In the X-ray picture montmorillonite is easily recognized by the shifting of the innermost interference corresponding to the swelling at varying water contents.

It has been suggested that the adsorption of the clays may be due to a common constituent, namely the layers of silicon atoms linked together in a silicon-oxygen sheet.

HOFMANN and his collaborators criticize on the basis of their findings the opinion held by O. ECKART and others that the bleaching power of the earths is due entirely to physical adsorption. The latter workers attribute the activation of the clays to the enlarging of the capillaries (the inner pore-surfaces) by the leaching out of various mineral salt constituents and consequently opening up of the structure. SCHOENFELD[64] assumed that production of, or increase in, decoloration power by boiling with mineral acid was caused by the setting free of active surfaces which in their natural condition were sealed with metal salts; he thus seeks to explain the process as similar to activation of carbon (see p. 107).

VAGELER and ENDELL[65] suggested that the mineral acid caused the exchangeable bases to be replaced by hydrogen ions, and FOGLE and OLIN[66] postulated for bleaching earth a structure similar to zeolites and attributed the activation to an exchange of Ca-ions against H-ions. HOFMANN and co-workers accepted this view and proved its accuracy by demonstrating that activation is not only possible with mineral acids, but also through electro-dialytic removal of the bases.

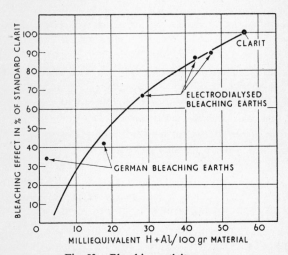

Fig. 53. Bleaching activity curve.

HOFMANN believes that the bleaching effect is due to the Al-ions on the surface of the clay particles, the so-called "clay acid" which abstracts by adsorption the colour particles with basic reaction from the oil and forms chemical compounds. The base-exchange power in milli-equivalents per 100 g dry matter is for montmorillonite 60–80, kaolinit (ceramic clay) only 3–15. Activation of the crude clay is then, according to HOFMANN and ENDELL[67], effected through the replacement of exchangeably bound bases, mainly calcium- and magnesium-ions by similarly bound hydrogen- and aluminium-ions.

Fig. 53 shows the bleaching activity of electro-dialysed and HCl-activated clay, indicated in per cent of the effect of a well-known HCl-activated German bleaching earth (Clarit). The horizontal axis shows the quantity of exchange-able hydrogen- and aluminium-ions in milli-equivalents per 100 g dry matter. The bleaching effect is a function of the H- and Al-ions in the earth.

It has still to be proved that all the colour particles in the fats can form

101

colour complexes with Al-ions; nor does HOFMANN'S hypothesis afford an explanation of the adsorption by the bleaching earth of taste-and-odour compounds.

ECKART [68] states that bleaching clay when heated loses water readily; the dehydration curve has a steep, nearly straight gradient. Ordinary clays, however, only give up most of their moisture when heated to 450–550°C. Table VIII shows moisture loss at various temperatures for three samples representing bleaching earths and a non-activatable kaolin.

TABLE VIII

	200°	300°	400°	500°	700°	900°
Zettlitz kaolin	0·6%	0·7%	0·8%	5·62%	13·4%	13·8%
Landau raw clay	0·9	2·76	3·84	4·5	7·18	9·1
Activated clay	1·4	2·24	3·3	4·3	5·3	7·06

The behaviour during heating should therefore make possible a distinction between ordinary clay and clay activatable with mineral acids.

Fig. 54, from an article by SCHULTZE[69], shows the moisture loss of three acid-activated clays, one of German origin A, two of American origin B and C as a function of temperature. Dehydration curves are also shown for mont-

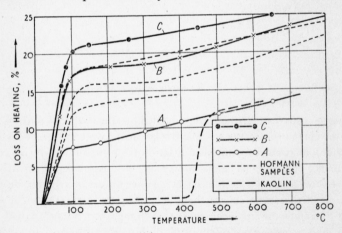

Fig. 54. Dehydration curves for bleaching earths.

morillonite and two samples of bentonite, calculated from data by HOFMANN and collaborators[70], and for a sample of kaolin. The dehydration of minerals with bleaching effect is in sharp contrast with that of the non-bleaching earth kaolin.

Another, but not very reliable, method of differentiating between bleaching clay and ordinary clay is, according to VOIGT[71], the thermo-effect when the clay is mixed with an unsaturated compound, for instance, turpentine. Voigt states, however, that the most reliable method is the recognition by X-rays of the montmorillonite structure and the one-dimensional swelling with water (according to U. Hofmann).

It is also useful to determine the exchangeability of the bases of the clay; it suffices as a first indication to ascertain the percentage solubility of Al_2O_3 and Fe_2O_3. If 16–18 per cent of the total sesqui-oxides dissolve in $N/2$ HCl by boiling for three hours, the clay should be suitable for activation.

By treatment with mineral acid three different reactions, according to Voigt, occur:

 (i) The acid first dissolves part of the Fe_2O_3 and Al_2O_3 (as well as of CaO, MgO, etc.) from the lattices; this causes an opening up of the crystal lattice and an increase in active surface.

 (ii) The second reaction is the gradual exchange of the Ca- and Mg-ions, located at the surface of the crystals, against hydrogen ions from the mineral acid.

(iii) A proportion of the hydrogen ions which have replaced Ca- and Mg-ions are exchanged against Al-ions in the solution.

The hydrogen ions which are exchangeably bound in the bleaching earth are, according to Kulkarni and Jatkar[72], exchanged against Na-ions on shaking with a salt solution. An NaCl extract from a bleaching earth shows therefore an acid pH value; for instance, the extract from Florida earth and from a German active earth had a pH value of 3·2–3·3. Slightly active earths gave NaCl extracts with correspondingly higher pH values.

3. *Manufacture of Bleaching Earths.*—The preparation of natural bleaching earths is fairly simple. The crude clay is separated from soil and other admixtures by sedimentation, the slurry filtered, dried and ground to the desired fineness.

The manufacture of activated earth by treating the bentonite clay with acid—hydrochloric is the acid mostly used, but sulphuric acid is sometimes employed—proceeds through a number of steps, involving grinding of the clay, suspending the powder in water, treating it with about 30 per cent of its weight, as dry matter, of concentrated HCl in suitable tanks, pumping the treated materials through filterpresses, washing the filtered paste in the presses, drying it in drums or rotating kilns, and finally grinding the dry powder in ball or hammer mills. The processes are described here on the basis of details given by Burghardt[73] and in official British and American Intelligence Objectives reports.[74].

Fig. 55 shows a flow-diagram for the process. The crude clay is made into a slurry in sedimentation tank *3*, which is provided with suitable paddle stirrers to break up the lumps. The slurry is passed via strainer box *4* and pump *5* to the activation tank *7*, where hydrochloric acid (in America sulphuric acid is also used) is added and the contents brought to the boil by means of open steam, admitted through a coil of acid-proof material.

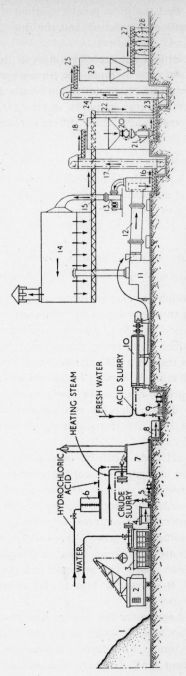

Fig. 55. Plant for activation of bleaching earth.

The acid is measured exactly in vessel *6* and the activation mixture boiled 2-3 hours at about 105°C.

The optimal ratio of acid and crude clay must be determined by laboratory tests for each kind of clay; that from the Isaar Valley in Bavaria usually requires 28-30 per cent HCl, calculated on waterfree clay, i.e., about 1 ton technical HCl of 19-21°Bé per ton finished bleaching earth.

The boiling vessel *7*, originally made of wood but in recent years frequently of metal clad with acid-proof tiles or bricks, has a volume of 20-30 M³ for a charge of 2-3 tons clay. All metal parts and fittings in the activation vessel must be of corrosion-proof material, for instance metal coated with hard rubber. The activated slurry, which after the reaction contains about 8 per cent HCl, is drawn from the bottom of the vessel and passed through a strainer box *8* to a slurry pump *9*, which presses it through a pitchpine or otherwise acid-proof filterpress *10*. The presscakes are washed with water in the press till free from acid, which takes about 6 hours. The frames in the press have a maximum thickness of 35 mm as thicker cakes are difficult to wash out.

A drying cylinder *12*, heated with combustion gases from coke oven *11*, which by exhausters *13* are blown through the cylinder, serves to dry the earth. The gases carry rather large quantities of dust away, which are precipitated in an electrostatic dust removal plant *14* and carried by a worm conveyor *15* to shaft *22*.

The dried cakes form lumps about the size of hazel nuts and fall from the drying cylinder into worm *16*, which takes the material to elevator *17*, conveyor *18* and on to silo *19* for the dried product. From this silo it reaches the grinding plant *21*, consisting of disintegrators, hammermills or ballmills, and the fineness of the powder is determined by the mesh of the sieve plate. Usually the particle size is such that 85-90 per cent passes a 110-mesh sieve and 100 per cent a 65-mesh.

The finished powder from the grinding plant is taken by conveyor *23*, elevator *24* and conveyor *25* to silo *26*, and from there to the bagging plant *27, 28*.

4. *Properties of Bleaching Earths.*—Commercial bleaching earths are yellow to yellowish-green or bluish-grey loose powders. The packing weights per litre of activated earths are, according to ECKART and WIRZMÜLLER[75], 0·7-1·2 kg, the true specific weight is 1·8-2·3. Natural fuller's earth, dried to 6-8 per cent moisture, has a litre-weight of 0·5-0·6 kg. In dry atmosphere the powders are of good stability, and do not lose activity even after prolonged storage.

The natural bleaching earths, and those activated earths which have been washed to complete neutrality, are quite inert towards the glycerides and do not change the chemical constants of the fat when bleaching them. Some grades of activated earths retain, in certain cases intentionally, small amounts of the mineral acid used for activation, and can when used cause a slight increase in the acidity of the fat. Such earths may also impart to the fat a

105

peculiar musty odour, often described as "earthy", which, however, is readily removed in subsequent deodorizing. The acid-reacting bleaching earths have also generally a higher decolorizing power than the neutral products. Washing-out of activated earth to complete neutrality involves great difficulty, and great care is necessary to remove the last traces of acid, which are retained tenaciously by the earth. The acid earths have also a tendency to weaken and attack the filter cloths in the presses used for separating the earth from the bleached fat. The filter cloths, particularly cotton cloths, have therefore a shorter life and thereby increase the filtration cost. Most commercial brands of activated earth are, however, nearly neutral, except certain brands for special purposes. The natural earths have the advantage not to cause increase in acidity of the fat, but their bleaching power is lower.

The very small particle size and fine capillary structure of the activated earths generally cause them to absorb and retain a high proportion of fat in the filterpress cake, up to 50 per cent or more, although this may be reduced by steam or air pressure on the press, or by displacement. The natural earths absorb less, 18–35 per cent. The rate of filtration is also slower with the finely ground activated earth than with the generally coarser natural earth.

In assessing the economic effect of bleaching earths on cost one must therefore consider, in addition to bleaching power, such factors as the action on the acidity of the fat, the effect on the filter cloths, the fat-retention in the filterpress cake, and the speed of filtration.

Of the many commercial supplies of natural bleaching earths may be mentioned the American Neutrol, Floridine and bentonites, the English Surrey fuller's earth, the German Frankonite S and Frisia, Carlonit from Czechoslovakia, Decoloro from Holland, Kambara earth from Japan, and various supplies from France, India, etc. Natural earths have lost a little in importance since the introduction of activated earths, although they still find wide use where high bleaching power is not necessary, for instance, on light-coloured fats, for clarification, or in mixtures with activated earth and, particularly, with activated carbons (see later).

Of activated earths much used in the refining industry may be mentioned the following brands: The American Super Filtrol, Special Filtrol and Activite; the English Activated Fuller's Earths and Fulmont Earths of *The Fuller's Earth Union*; the German earths, Alsil, Clarit, Frankonit, Isarit, Montana, Tonsil, Terrana; the French Clarsil, and products from various countries with principally local use. Many of the mentioned brands are sold in several varieties, differing in acidity, particle size, bleaching power and fat retention; for some, specific activity on certain oils and fats, and within certain temperature ranges, is claimed.

Spent bleaching earth, i.e., the filterpress cake residues after bleaching, can be given a regeneration treatment after removal of the absorbed oil and organic impurities, in order to revive the bleaching power. Numerous processes have been proposed and many patents recorded. They consist in a

106

roasting and ashing treatment in suitable furnaces, but experience appears to show, that a product equivalent to the original is not obtained. Regenerated earth, even when mixed with a large proportion of fresh earth, often imparts to the filtered bleached oil a taste and odour, which is very difficult to remove completely by deodorization, and it is therefore not quite suitable for high-grade edible products. It can, however, in many cases be used for technical fats or for clarification. As the regeneration process is complicated and costly it is not often used. It is, on the other hand, general practice to recover as far as possible the fatty matter from the filterpress residue (see p. 125) and discard the extracted earth.

As the full bleaching power of the earth is rarely exhausted after a bleaching operation, the residue after filtration from the bleached oil can be used to remove some of the colour from a further charge of high-coloured oil of the same kind, but in that case great care must be taken that no air or moisture gains access to the press-cake, as oxidation of the oil in the cake takes place easily and may cause noticeable deterioration in the next charge. It is also necessary for the oil to be thoroughly purified before neutralization and bleaching, as otherwise there may be present in the residue soaps, mucilage, etc., which will have a potentially harmful effect on the next charge. The utilization of the residual bleaching power in the filter cake in the unopened press has been the basis of a semi-continuous bleaching process, to which reference will be made later.

Decolorizing Carbons

The industrial production of "activated carbon" from charcoal, peat and other carbonaceous materials by artificial increase of their interior surfaces dates back to the time of the first world war. The products which principally consist of carbon are noted for their very high adsorptive power towards compounds of widely different types, such as organic dyes, vapour, gases, colloids, etc. The earliest known product of this type, which has found technical use, was bonechar, prepared by charring of de-fatted bones; it has been used since about 1820 for decoloration of sugar juice. The modern activated carbons have, however, a much higher adsorptive power than bonechar.

The carbons made by carbonizing wood in kilns or retorts have only low adsorption effect, but they serve as important raw materials for production of activated products of very high adsorptive capacity. The activation of the various carbonaceous materials is explained as being due to opening up of the pores, which in the usual carbons are filled with "tar"—hydrocarbons and similar organic compounds. If these fillings are eliminated by oxidation or coking in such a manner that no tarry matters arise and are retained in the carbon, products are obtained which have a very much extended surface. These new surfaces vary, according to MECKLENBURG[76], with the raw material and method of production, which explains the properties of the different activated carbons. These variations are probably due not only to disparity in surface developments, but also to differences in the chemical character of the surface layers.

MECKLENBURG stated that the quality of the active carbons depended on the size of surface area and on capillary volume per unit weight, the cross-sectional area of the capillaries, the particle size, the chemical character of the surface, the nature of the adsorbent, etc. The magnitude of the surface extension of active carbon was measured by the degree of absorption of methylene blue from aqueous solutions. By this method inner surfaces of active carbons of 200–650 m^2/g were found. In the laboratory active carbons with surfaces up to 1250 m^2/g could be made[77].

Activated carbons are excellent decolorisers for certain fats, particularly in mixtures with bleaching earths; not only is their bleaching power for various fats high, but their degree of decoloration is generally much higher than that of bleaching earth alone. The activated carbons are capable, in a much higher degree than the bleaching earths, of absorbing flavours and odours and contribute substantially to quality improvement of the fat. For instance, the "earthy" or "musty" odour which the activated earths often impart to oils is not caused when mixtures of earth and activated carbon are used for bleaching. It is, however, peculiar that some carbons, which have a particularly good bleaching effect on certain fats, such as coconut oil and palm-kernel oil, show no noticeably better results on other fats than do bleaching earths.

The oil retention of activated carbon is higher than that of activated clays, i.e., it retains more than equal weight of oil in the filterpress cake, but owing to the very high bleaching power smaller proportions are used than of bleaching earth, and therefore the total loss in the filterpress cake may be less. Filtration is, however, more difficult and slower, which is one of the reasons why carbon is frequently used in mixture with bleaching earth, which improves the rate of filtration. It has been found by experience that a mixture of activated carbon with natural bleaching earth in the ratio 1:8 to 1:10 has practically the same bleaching effect as activated carbon alone in the same amount as the mixture. As the cost of the carbon is much higher than that of natural and activated earth, the use of the mixture is obviously much more economical.

1. *Manufacture of Activated Carbon.*—R. v. OSTREYKO in Poland was the inventor of activated decolorizing carbons[78]. He observed at the beginning of this century that highly active adsorbents could be obtained by heating charcoal and other carbonaceous materials with steam, carbon dioxide and other oxygen-yielding gases, or by treatment with zinc chloride, alkali carbonates, etc. By these observations he indicated exactly the two methods, which have since formed the principal technical processes for making activated carbons. The industry developed rapidly during the 1914–1918 war owing to the great demand for adsorbents for respirators and gas adsorption. The carbonaceous raw materials were largely shells of coconuts and stony fruit kernels.

According to OSTREYKO'S invention, one can distinguish between gas-activated and chemically activated carbons, which differ not only in the activation agents but also in their action. For activation by oxygen-containing gases various kinds of coal, particularly charcoal, serve as raw materials; by the action of the gases the organic compounds contained in the pores, as well as some of the carbon, are burned away by oxidation. In the chemical activation with zinc chloride, etc., the raw material is mostly sawdust and cellulosic material, and activation is effected by the removal of the elements of water, so that only minor amounts of tar can be formed. Peat and various kinds of coal can also be used for chemical activation.

In the direct method of activation by oxidizing gases the carbonaceous material is crushed and screened to a particle size of about $\frac{1}{8}$ in. and charged into a retort and treated generally with steam, whereby organic compounds such as hydrocarbons are rapidly, and amorphous coal only slowly, oxidized. Other oxidizing gases such as carbon dioxide, air, sulphur dioxide and combustion gases can also be used, but steam is preferred and gives the best activated carbon. The reaction is in principle similar to the water gas reaction, $C + H_2O \rightleftarrows CO + H_2$, and is endothermic. The resulting mixture of carbon monoxide and hydrogen can be used for additional heating of the activation plant and for generation of steam.

The activation takes place at 800–1,000°C in 4–5 m high retorts of refractory material, a battery of 4–6 retorts being provided with common heating. Steam is admitted to the retorts from the bottom or through the sides, while the crushed charcoal is charged from the top at the rate of withdrawal of the finished carbon from the bottom. 1 part coal requires about 1·5 parts steam for activation, and the process takes 4–10 hours; the more steam is used, the better is the carbon activated; the yield, however, decreases with increasing activation as larger quantities of raw material is converted into water gas. The yields are between 15 per cent and 25 per cent of the original material.

In America methods have been developed in which the crushed raw material is charged continuously to a vertical 7 in. nichrome tube in which activation takes place. An outer retort, in which gas is burned, surrounds the inner tube, which is provided with a perforated central nichrome tube through which superheated steam is admitted. Gas in the outer retort heats the charcoal to 800–1,000°C. In another method the crushed carbonaceous material is placed in trays on trucks which are wheeled into a kiln and kept at 850°C for about 4 hours. These methods are stated to give higher yields and more uniform products.

In Britain, after the raw material has been carbonized at 450–500°C, activation is done with steam in vertical retorts at 950–1,000°C until about 75 per cent of the coal has been burned away as gas, for which purpose 200–300 per cent steam is needed, and a yield of activated carbon equal to about 12·5 per cent of the original coal is obtained.

When air is used in the activation process the reaction is exothermic and

109

difficult to control. Mixtures of air and steam, or steam alone, are therefore preferred.

A wider range of coals can be used in the "briquetting" process. The charcoal is ground and mixed with an equal weight of tar and about 1 per cent caustic soda, compressed and extruded as pellets, packed in wire trays on trucks, which are wheeled into kilns, where the material is hardened by being heated to 100°C. It passes then through two rotary kilns in series, in the first of which it is heated to about 160°C and in the second to 550°C; the waste gases from the latter are used to heat the former. The carbonized pellets pass to a third rotary kiln, where activation with superheated steam at 1,000°C takes place. Finally the product is cooled out of contact with air prior to grinding. This method is stated to be used for the well-known activated carbons of the *Norit Company* in Holland.

For "chemical" activation zinc chloride or phosphoric acid is mostly used in practice, but calcium chloride, magnesium chloride, alkali carbonate, sulphuric acid, etc., have also found application. These methods give high yields. The zinc chloride method is used in the manufacture of Carboraffine by the *Carbo-Norit-Union* in Germany. Wood chips or sawdust is mixed with about 2·7 parts zinc chloride solution of 60°Bé, the mixture dried and carbonized in rotary retorts at temperatures exceeding 600°C. The resulting carbon, which still contains appreciable quantities of zinc salts and zinc oxide, is extracted with acid and washed with water, dried and ground.

The French *Compagnie des Produits Chimiques et Carbons Actifs Ed. Urbain* uses as raw material peat of low ash content, which is ground and mixed to a paste with phosphoric acid of 50 per cent strength. Extrusion of this produces threads which are dried by waste gases in rotary kilns, broken into short pellets and heated in gas retorts at 1,000°C for 6–8 hours, cooled, washed with hydrochloric acid and water and finally dried at 300°C and ground. Activation is caused by reduction of the phosphoric acid.

2. *Properties of Activated Carbons.*—Carbons activated by the direct or gas method and by the chemical method show certain differences in their physical and chemical properties. The gas-activated carbons still show the structure of the raw materials—for instance, the wood structure—whereas the chemically activated products are structureless. Steam-activated carbons have an alkaline reaction, while those activated with zinc chloride or acid give water extracts with acid reaction. A slight acidity may interfere with the decoloration of sugar solutions, as the disappearance of an alkaline reaction in the sugar juice may entail the risk of formation of invert sugar. It is therefore customary to mix carbon for bleaching sugar juice with slaked lime. When used for bleaching fats the slight acidity of the activated carbons is of no practical importance, firstly because the carbons are rarely used in greater proportions than 0·1–0·2 per cent, and secondly because the traces of mineral acid in the washed carbons are held so strongly by adsorption, that they are not given up to the fats; the release of acid is only possible in an aqueous medium; in fact, the acid-reacting carbons adsorb from fats,

containing free fatty acids, a certain proportion of these acids, in contrast to the acid-reacting activated bleaching earths. The true density of these carbons is 2·2–2·3, but the bulk density is much lower, 0·3–0·5.

Of the well-known brands which have found use in the bleaching of oils and fats may be mentioned the various grades of Norit, made by the *Norit Company* in various countries, as well as the same company's brands Purit and Esbit, Carboraffine, the French products of the *Ed. Urbain Company*, the American Nuchar, and the British activated vegetable carbons of *Sutcliffe & Speakman & Co. Ltd.*

Use of Bleaching Earths and Carbons

Decoloration with adsorbents is done by two methods, the "batch mixing" process and the "fixed filter bed" process. In the former the liquid is mixed, generally at elevated temperature, for a certain time with the adsorbent, which is then separated from the decolorized liquid by filtration. In the latter process the warm liquid is passed through successive layers or filter beds of 7–10 mm thickness of the adsorbent, until the desired degree of decoloration has been achieved.

The industrial decoloration of fats is almost entirely by the batch-mixing process. The neutralized fat is mixed with the appropriate amount of adsorbent at 70–90°C, with some fats temperatures up to 130–140°C are used, for varying periods, usually 20–40 mins., and preferably in vacuum. The temperature of the fat is then adjusted to that most suitable for filtration, the vacuum broken, and the mixture pumped through the filterpress while continued stirring keeps the adsorbent in suspension.

While "fixed bed" filtration is suitable for aqueous liquids such as sugar juice, it is, as stated, unsuitable for fats, where either bleaching earth alone or mixtures of this with small proportions of decolorizing carbon are used. While on aqueous liquids a higher bleaching effect has been ascertained in "fixed bed" filtration with carbons, this has not been the case with earth. Furthermore, the rate of filtration is slower and large filter surfaces are required. To avoid the very large filtration surfaces of the usual "fixed bed" filter layers, the process might be divided into two stages by first applying batch mixing with bleaching earth and then passing the filtrate from the first stage over filter beds of activated carbon. H. SCHOENFELD has obtained good results on pre-bleached coconut oil by running this at a rate of 80–100 litres per hour per square metre over a carbon filter layer of 7–10 mm thickness. For decolorizing 20 tons oil per 24 hours two small filters of about 15–20 square metres surface would suffice.

Decoloration of pre-bleached oil on carbon filter-beds would have a further advantage. As bleaching power depends on the concentration of colouring matter in the oil to be bleached, it is clear that an adsorbent whose power of decolorizing a certain oil is exhausted, will still be able to reduce the colour of a darker oil; therefore, partly spent decolorizing carbon from the bleaching of neutral oils can still be used for bleaching darker crude oils of same kind.

111

In the batch mixing process a two-stage use of the adsorbent would require the installation of a second bleaching apparatus.

Before being treated on partly spent carbon beds the crude oils would have to be de-gummed, as carbon adsorbents possess in still higher degree than bleaching earths the property of precipitating mucilage from the oils. Filtration of slimy oil through a carbon layer will soon cause the filter surface to become coated with a thin layer of colloidal matter, which raises the resistance to filtration, even before the decolorizing power of the carbon has been partly utilized.

Evaluation and Selection of Adsorbents

Differences in the adsorption constants (see p. 94) at varying temperatures and towards fats of different kinds, and even towards different consignments of the same kind of fat, makes it often desirable to carry out explora-

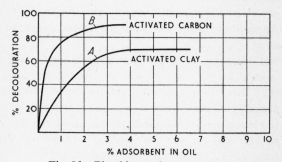

Fig. 56. Bleaching performance curve.

tory laboratory tests to ascertain the type and proportion of adsorbent, which is most suitable and economical to use to achieve the desired degree of decoloration. As the temperature, the type of agitation and other factors also play a part, laboratory results cannot always be reproduced on industrial scale, but strictly standardized laboratory tests can be made to correlate sufficiently with works practice to serve as a guide.

Fig. 56 shows bleaching curves for two adsorbents differing in performance, as obtained in experiments by PICK and KRAUS[79]. Fig. 57 shows curves for two adsorbents more similar in performance, but slightly different in activity[80].

In Fig. 56 the curve A refers to an activated clay, curve B to a highly activated decolorizing carbon. From these curves it will be seen—

1. That up to 65 per cent decoloration the oil can be bleached with A or B, but B is superior within the whole bleaching range. B gives a much higher degree of bleaching than the same proportion of A, and therefore to achieve the same degree of bleaching smaller proportions of B are needed.

112

2. That the weaker decolorizer A has a much smaller bleaching range than the more active B. In this case bleaching beyond 70 per cent cannot be attained with A, whereas B can be used to 90 per cent decoloration.

Similar considerations apply to the curves for adsorbents A_1 and B_1 in Fig. 57. Above the point of intersection of the horizontal line M with curve A_1 this adsorbent has practically no further bleaching effect; if a higher degree of bleaching is required, it can only be obtained with adsorbent B_1.

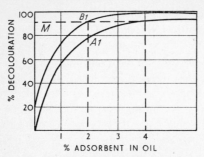

Fig. 57. Bleaching activity curves.

For the performance or value ratio of adsorbents A and B different figures are found, according to whether the ratios are based on equal quantities used (the equal weight method) or on equal decoloration (the equal performance method). This is illustrated by the figures in Tables W and P, derived from Fig. 56.

TABLE W				TABLE P			
Performance Ratio of A and B on "Equal Weight" Basis				Value Ratio of A and B on "Equal Performance" Basis			
Quantity (%) Used	Decoloration in (%)		Value Ratio	Decoloration in (%)	Quantity Used (%)		Value Ratio
	B	A			B	A	
0·5	62	19	3·26	20	0·07	0·50	7·14
1·0	76	34	2·23	40	0·18	1·23	6·83
2·0	85	55	1·54	60	0·45	2·34	5·20
3·0	90	66	1·36	70	0·70	4·20	6·00
				80	1·30	∞	∞

Comparison of different adsorbents by the "equal weight" method gives, as will be seen, deceptive values. Thus for a 90 per cent decoloration the more active adsorbent would give a value ratio of 1·36, although such a degree of decoloration would be impossible with the less active one, and on "equal performance" the ratio for decoloration is infinite above 70 per cent.

To compare performance of equal quantities of adsorbent is rarely of practical value, as the question is frequently how much is required of an adsorbent to give a fat the particular colour desired, i.e., to achieve a certain degree of decoloration.

From Table P it will also be seen that there is no definite constant value ratio of two adsorbents and that the ratio varies with the degree of decoloration. But a still more important factor to consider is the oil whose nature, previous treatment and history may cause wide variations in the ratio and perhaps entirely upset it, so that, for instance, the adsorbents A and B in Fig. 56 when tested on another oil change positions. It is sometimes found with certain oils that the normally more active carbon has no better effect than, and is even inferior to, bleaching earths. It is therefore not possible to give rigid rules as to the most suitable adsorbents for the different fats, and exploratory laboratory tests serve to indicate which adsorbent is preferable for a particular oil, and whether activated carbons offer advantages.

Many control laboratories use for evaluation of adsorbents a standard product, either an official standard or one selected by experience, against which new consignments or new brands are compared. The value ratio of the adsorbent under test and the standard is often termed the "oil factor". It is, however, not enough to establish the oil factor for bleaching earth alone or for carbon alone. Practical experience has shown[81], that on some fats, particularly neutralized coconut oil, the value ratio of carbon to bleaching earth increases noticeably in favour of carbon when decoloration is effected by a mixture of the two adsorbents.

When neutralized oils are used for comparing the effects of bleaching with equal quantities of carbon and bleaching earth, it is often observed that by medium decoloration (for instance, on coconut oil) the activated carbon is somewhat superior to bleaching earth, but at the level of intense decoloration the superiority is much more marked. In other words, the superiority of decolorizing carbon is much greater at a higher degree of decoloration, as shown in Fig. 56.

From these experiments the conclusions might be drawn that the activated carbons, which are much more expensive than the bleaching earths, could only be used more economically than the earths above certain degrees of decoloration. But that conclusion only applies when the separate adsorbents are used.

Much more favourable oil factors for carbons are obtained when mixtures, in which the carbons form only a minor proportion, are compared for bleaching effect with pure bleaching earths. In such cases the carbons show also with slight decoloration a high value ratio. For example, on neutral coconut oil 0·5 per cent bleaching earth + 0·02 per cent activated carbon often shows equal or higher decolorizing power than 1 per cent earth alone, which indicates for the carbon a value ratio of 25 times that of bleaching earth.

The explanation is that the various colouring compounds in the oils have different affinities for the different adsorbents; those more easily removed are well adsorbed by the bleaching earth, while the higher adsorbing power of the activated carbon is applied towards those more difficult to remove. The adsorbents possess also a certain selectiveness towards the different colour compounds, some being preferentially adsorbed by the bleaching earth, some by the carbon. The selective action of the two kinds of adsorbents can be demonstrated, for instance, by bleaching cottonseed oil to equal degrees of decoloration with earth and with carbon; when the bleached oils are compared in the Lovibond tintometer they show different ratios of Red and Yellow.

The selection of the most suitable decolorizer for a particular oil is generally based on the following points:

If bleaching earth alone is considered, the quality is chosen which in equal quantity gives the best decoloration, as shown by preliminary experiments. At the same time regard must be had to oil retention, acidity effect and price.

If the oil is one that requires treatment with a mixture of earth and carbon, the most effective and economical ratio of the two materials must be determined by means of the bleaching curves of (1) constant quantities of earth with varying quantities of carbon, and (2) constant quantities of carbon with varying quantities of earth[82]. The first set of curves may, for instance, be drawn from three tests with 0·5 per cent earth mixed with 0·05 per cent, 0·1 per cent and 0·15 per cent carbon, the second set from 0·1 per cent carbon mixed with 0·5 per cent, 0·75 per cent and 1 per cent earth. The curves obtained in this way should, of course, cover the range of decoloration required.

The cost of bleaching can then be calculated for points of equal decoloration, and, as already pointed out, in addition to the price of the adsorbents consideration must also be given to oil retention, degradation of oil in filterpress residue, etc.

Attempts have been made[75] to establish a set of rules for selecting for the various kinds of fats and oils the most suitable adsorbent, its proportion and the best operating temperature, but such rules can only be used as approximate pointers. Most refiners base their preferences on their own experience, which often depends on the plant available and general working conditions, and they frequently use the same kind of adsorbent on a number of different fats and oils. The amount used then depends on the kind of fat, its original colour and the degree of bleaching wanted. As mentioned under neutralization, the refiner attempts to achieve as high a degree as possible of decoloration in that process, and this often saves appreciably in cost of adsorbents. A badly pre-treated fat requires much more bleaching material.

Ready mixtures of bleaching earth and activated carbon are marketed, but most refiners prefer to purchase the individual adsorbents and, if mixtures are wanted, prepare them in such ratios as are considered most effective.

It should be emphasized that decoloration, although the most important, is not the only function of the adsorbents; they retain colloidal matter, traces of soap from neutralization, and they adsorb taste and odour compounds or change some of them and make them easier to remove by deodorization. It is the experience of many refiners that a well and properly bleached oil is easier to deodorize than one which is insufficiently treated with adsorbents.

To obtain the benefit of this deodorizing effect and to ease filtration by the formation of a good filter bed in the filterpress mixtures of natural bleaching earth and activated carbon are very useful, particularly on light-coloured fats, such as coconut oil, palm kernel oil and similar fats, where the proportion of adsorbent needed for bleaching would be very small, if provided by activated carbon alone. Besides, some colouring matters in these fats are difficult to remove except by activated carbon. Consequently a combination of 8–10 parts of natural earth and 1 part of activated carbon has, by experience, been found very effective and economical to bleach the fats mentioned, for instance, 1·5 per cent earth plus 0·2 per cent carbon, and this mixture gives practically the same effect as if the whole quantity of adsorbent consisted of activated carbon, and it makes it much easier to obtain a clear filtrate. The saving on the expensive carbon exceeds the cost of the larger amount of fat absorbed in the filter residue.

The laboratory tests for evaluating adsorbents or for determining the bleachability of oils are standardized in some countries, where the results form the basis of commercial contracts. Many refiners have their own tests which experience has shown correlate with plant scale operation. Such a test may, for instance, be carried out in the following manner:

200 g of oil or fat are weighed into a beaker of non-transparent material, such as enamelled metal, stainless steel or porcelain, and provided with a stirrer that can be rotated at about 300 r.p.m. and is shaped to ensure intimate mixing of the adsorbent with the oil. The beaker is covered so that the contents can be blanketed with an inert gas, and a thermometer for temperatures up to 180°C is provided. The oil in the beaker is warmed to about 70°C in 5 mins. while stirring. After stopping the stirrers the weighed amount of adsorbent is quickly added, stirring restarted and the temperature rapidly brought to that at which the test should be carried out and kept constantly there for 20–60 mins. Heating is discontinued and the contents cooled to 80°C under a blanket of inert gas. Stirring is now stopped and the contents of the beaker poured on to a folded filter paper placed in a jacketed funnel which can be covered to maintain the inert atmosphere during filtration. The colour of the filtered oil is determined by one of the standardized methods of colorimetry.

By this test indications can be obtained of the most suitable period and temperature of contact as well as of the proportion of adsorbent for the particular oil. Some require temperatures as high as 130–140°C to show maximum decoloration, but filtration should not take place above 80–90°C.

A comparative test for oil retention can be made by carrying out a bleaching test with a fixed percentage of adsorbent, for instance, 10 per cent, and filtering in a Büchner jacketed funnel at a fixed temperature (50°C) until no more oil comes through. The percentage of oil retained in the filter cake is then analysed by an accepted method, for instance, solvent extraction or ash determination, or otherwise ascertained.

As the amount of free mineral acid left in the adsorbent after activation may affect the bleaching power towards certain fats as well as the tendency to cause some hydrolysis in the fat and to attack the filter cloth, it is customary to examine it for free acidity. One method consists in determining the number of mls of deci-normal caustic alkali required to neutralize the aqueous extract from 100 g of adsorbent. The figures vary between nil and 15 ml for earths. Some activated carbons may show slight alkalinity.

Although tests as those described, when done by standardized procedure, generally provide valuable information about the results which may be expected from the bleaching process, it is at times found that some adsorbents, which in the bleaching process are less effective than others, leave the filtered oil in a condition in which it responds more readily to the further heat-bleaching effect of deodorization, so that while apparently less decolorized by bleaching the final deodorized oil shows a paler colour. There is, however, also sometimes the opposite effect, that an oil darkens during deodorization. It is therefore essential that a final verdict regarding the suitability of a certain bleaching treatment is not given, until the final process of the oil is completed.

Plant and Processes for Bleaching

While some refiners still use open vessels for bleaching of fats and oils, the introduction of the highly activated adsorbents, and the need with some fats for operating at rather high temperature, entails a risk of oxidation of unsaturated glycerides. Modern plant is therefore nearly always constructed for working in high or partial vacuum.

The vertical vessels shown in Figs. 32 and 33 are of the type known as neutralizer-bleacher, as they serve the double purpose, and the fat, after neutralization and washing, remains in the same vessel for bleaching. The oil is heated by the closed steam coils and can, if desired, be dried in vacuum before bleaching. The adsorbent is drawn in by the vacuum through a pipe at the top; this is usually sufficiently long to discharge the adsorbent under the surface of the oil to avoid the light powdery material being drawn into the vacuum line. The agitators should revolve fast enough to maintain an intimate mixture during bleaching, and should be of such construction that they prevent any settling of adsorbent at the bottom when the vessel is being emptied.

Fig. 58 shows a diagram of a vessel, arranged for washing and bleaching. A circular pipe at the top with spray nozzles provides the washing arrange-

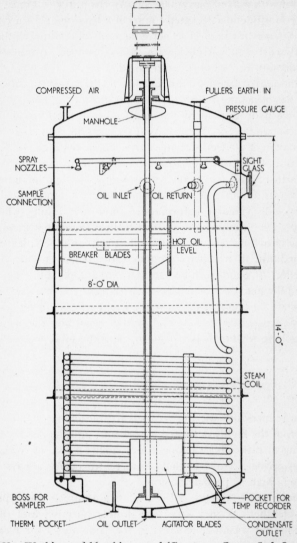

Fig. 58. Washing and bleaching vessel (Courtesy: *Bamag Ltd., London*).

ment. The oil inlet is taken well down into the vessel and a second inlet permits oil, which emerges cloudy from the filterpress, to be returned to the bleaching vessel. Compressed air can be supplied at the top to enable filtration to be done under air pressure.

Horizontal vessels, as that shown in Fig. 59, are recommended by some makers. They are heated by a steam jacket which covers the lower half. They are not usable as neutralizers, but require less power for stirring, which is generally done by a spiral paddle arrangement. A dome on the top connects up with the vacuum arrangement. The adsorbent is drawn in at one end through a pipe from the top which dips well into the oil.

Bleaching vessels must be absolutely airtight, particularly below the oil level, as air leaking into the hot oil, especially in the presence of the adsorbent, may cause oxidative deterioration in the oil. The bleacher must therefore be tested frequently for air-tightness by evacuating the empty vessel and observing its capacity for maintaining vacuum with all in- and outlets closed. There is more risk in working with a leaky vacuum vessel than in doing the

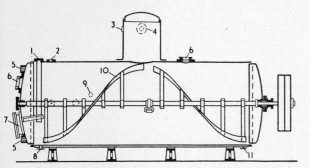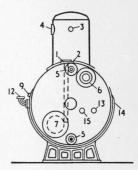

Fig. 59. Horizontal bleacher, according to *Harburger Eisen- und Bronzewerke*.

1. Earth inlet.	6. Inspection glass.	11. Drain for condensate.
2. Oil inlet.	7. Manhole.	12. Safety valve.
3. Vacuum gauge.	8. Oil outlet.	13. Sample cock.
4. Vacuum connection.	9. Vent.	14. Heating jacket.
5. Level gauge.	10. Stirrer.	15. Thermometer.

bleaching in an open vessel. Particular attention should be given to the tight closing of the bottom outlet valve, where particles of bleaching earth may lodge when the vessel is emptied.

It has long been accepted that the oil should be thoroughly dried before the adsorbent is added in order to obtain the full benefit of the decolorizing power of the latter. In many cases there is, however, strong evidence that to get maximum bleaching result the oil should contain a trace of moisture. This condition is, as a rule, attained if the neutralized oil is put under vacuum without being heated, when it will have lost its excess moisture and have the right starting temperature by the time the vacuum is high enough to draw in the adsorbent. The trace of moisture in the oil may cause the adsorbent to acquire an electric charge, and through the electrostatic force aid the initial adsorption of colour.

When the adsorbent is drawn in and mixed with the oil the temperature is increased as rapidly as possible to that desired for bleaching and kept at that temperature for the necessary time for the decoloration aimed at.

119

Bleaching time limits are mostly 20–60 mins., and while the temperatures are usually between 70° and 100°C it is not uncommon, particularly in America, for temperatures up to 135–140°C to be used.

Sometimes it is recommended not to add all the adsorbent in one charge, but to add first a smaller proportion of it to adsorb traces of soap and colloidal matter that may have passed through the neutralization treatment. The temperature is then adjusted for bleaching while the rest of the adsorbent is drawn in. A similar procedure is often adopted when both bleaching earth and carbon are used; part of the earth is first added, and finally the rest of the earth and the carbon as a mixture.

After bleaching, the contents of the vessel are cooled to a temperature low enough to avoid oxidation risk by exposing the oil to air, but still high enough to allow it to flow easily through the filterpress. The vacuum is then broken, and while the agitators are kept moving sufficiently fast to keep the adsorbent evenly suspended without beating in air, the mixture is filtered, preferably in frame presses or leaf filters, either by air pressure from the bleaching vessel or by pump pressure. In the latter case the pumps should give a steady flow, if necessary by inserting air vessels in the pressure line to avoid pulsations, which give uneven filtration and may cause strain on the filter cloths. Centrifugal pumps are very suitable. The smoothest filtration is achieved by air pressure.

It is often useful to cover the filter cloths on frame presses with a layer of filter paper to obtain a clearer filtrate, as well as to lessen wear on the cloths. The press cake between the paper surfaces is easily removed with the paper when filtration is finished, and the cloths can generally be used for several filtrations before they require cleaning.

To avoid solidification of solid fats, particularly the higher-melting hydrogenated fats, presses can be fitted with steam-heated headplates, and on long presses a number of intermediate plates can also be fitted with means for heating.

The "first runnings" through the press are usually turbid from fine particles of bleaching material passing through the cloths, until the adsorbent has formed a filter bed on the cloths. The "first runnings" are kept separate from the clear filtrate and returned to the bleaching vessel for re-filtration. To keep turbid and clear filtrate separate, the collecting troughs of the press can be divided longitudinally by a partition plate and the outlet cocks provided with hinged spouts, so that the flow from them can be directed to either of the two compartments and, if turbid, be returned to the bleacher or, if clear, be passed to the bleached oil tanks. The latter should preferably be of tinned or glass-lined steel or of some metal which does not impair the colour of the fat, and they should be covered or, in special cases, arranged for vacuum.

The dimensions of the presses should be calculated to permit filtration to be finished in 1–1½ hours. If the proportion of adsorbent plus the oil retained in the press cake would necessitate a longer time, it is advisable to filter through two presses in parallel. As an example may be mentioned that a plant for treating 30 tons oil per day would require two presses with about 30 chambers of 800 mm square.

When filtration is finished and the chambers in the press are filled with filter residue, in which there is a high proportion of loose and absorbed oil, air or steam pressure is applied to force through as much as possible of this oil. Either method has its disadvantages. Great care must be exercised when blowing with air, as some oxidation takes place by the air passing the pores of the highly active surface; the residual oil that is not forced out by the pressure is therefore of rather poor quality, and with semi-drying and drying oils, such as cottonseed, soya bean and linseed oils, excessive heating by oxidation can even lead to smouldering or fires; the safest is to cut off air pressure as soon as oil ceases to flow freely. With steam this risk is absent, and the greater wetting power of the steam towards the adsorbent enables a higher percentage of oil to be recovered, but the recovered oil also contains oxidation products, and the press cake as well as the oil is damp, and some hydrolysis of the oil may take place, particularly if traces of soap have been present. Furthermore, a trace of free mineral acid in the adsorbent may cause the steam to attack and weaken the filter cloth rather rapidly.

Whether air or steam is used for recovering the loosely held oil in the press chambers, it is advisable to keep these "last runnings" separate, as their presence in the bulk of the oil in later treatments may jeopardize quality.

The filterpress residue, after the press is emptied, still contains a high percentage of oil, the amount depending on the adsorbent used and the air or steam pressure applied, and may be between 18 per cent and 55 per cent. It must either be well spread out in a cool place for rapid cooling or be protected against long exposure in bulk to the air as the oil in its finely dispersed form in the adsorbent rapidly oxidizes, in the case of some oils to the point of ignition. If the residue is intended for treatment for recovery of the residual oil (see p. 125) it must be kept in closed containers.

Where adsorption bleaching is applied to low-grade dark coloured fats, such as technical tallow, bone grease, semi-hard and hard palm oil, etc., large proportions of adsorbent are necessary, sometimes 10 per cent or more, and it is often advisable to give low-grade animal fats a boiling-up treatment with sulphuric acid followed by washing out with water of traces of acid before bleaching. A very effective process of this type on tallows and palm oil is the combination of acid and adsorbent treatment in one operation by mixing the fat with 8–10 per cent natural bleaching earth and 0·2 per cent concentrated sulphuric acid in a vacuum vessel under intensive stirring at 115–125°C for about one hour. A small increase in free fatty acids is usual, but this is mostly unimportant with technical fats.

Acid oils and fatty acids, recovered from soapstock by splitting with mineral acid, are also often treated for colour improvement by bleaching with 5–10 per cent bleaching earth, and it is also here often effective to add towards the end of the operation a small percentage of dilute sulphuric acid,

9

or the acid in concentrated form can be added with the earth at the beginning. As the material in the filterpress in these cases is strongly acid, it is necessary to use a good quality woollen cloth, as cotton filter cloths are too rapidly destroyed by the acid earth and free fatty acids. Frame presses built of wood are also often used to avoid corrosion of the metal and the formation of metal soaps which cause discoloration and catalyze oxidation.

A process for continuous vacuum bleaching of oils has been described by KING and WHARTON[83]. The adsorbent is continuously mixed in the desired proportion with the oil at 55°C to form a slurry, and pumped through a spraying device into the upper section of a vertical cylindrical vessel kept under reduced pressure of 30 mm abs., where the slurry flashes off moisture

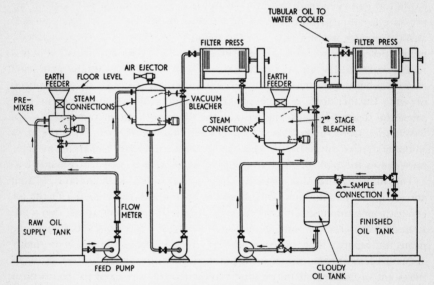

Fig. 60. Foster-Wheeler continuous bleaching process.

and gases and remains about 7 mins. It is then pumped through a heat exchanger, where it is heated to 105–115°C, and sprayed into the lower section of the vessel, where gaseous decomposition products and released moisture are removed. After about 10 mins. in the lower section the mixture is pumped through two closed filterpresses in series and subsequently cooled to 65°C before it is exposed to air. The de-aeration of the mixture before it is heated to bleaching temperature is considered very important, and in a mixture of adsorbent and oil flashing has been found the most effective way at the relatively low temperature. The short time of contact of oil and adsorbent is considered an advantage in reducing the effect of possible residual oxygen on oxidation.

A continuous bleaching plant is made by the *Foster-Wheeler Corporation* to work on the principle shown in the flowsheet in Fig. 60. The oil is pumped via a heater to a pre-mixer where adsorbent in the right ratio is added. The slurry is next drawn into a vacuum bleacher for a first bleaching treatment at an abs. pressure of about 75–150 mm and passes continuously to a filter-press, from which the filtered oil runs to a second bleacher, where fresh adsorbent is added while the mixture is heated further. The slurry is now pumped through a cooler to a second filterpress, from which "first runnings" and "cloudy" oil runs to a "cloudy oil" tank for re-filtration, while clear oil runs to the bleached oil tank. It is claimed that less adsorbent is used than in the batch bleaching process, and that by using small vessel units limited quantities are in circulation and therefore change from one quality to another is relatively easy.

According to the adsorption equation the amount of colouring matter adsorbed per unit of adsorbent increases with the concentration of the colouring matter at the equilibrium. There should therefore be a saving in adsorbent in a counter-current bleaching system, and several arrangements have been proposed for that purpose. HASSLER and HAGBERG[84] recorded some experimental work which indicated that this principle could be applied to bleaching of oil and effect a saving in adsorbent and oil retention. Where the bleaching is done in multiple stages and counter-current at atmospheric pressure, there is, however, the danger of oxidation effect on the colour and flavour by the residual oil in the adsorbent, and to obtain the expected advantages this system of bleaching should be carried out in a vacuum.

A plant for a continuous two-stage counter-current method of bleaching in vacuum has been designed by *The Girdler Corporation*[85] and is now in operation industrially. A vertical cylindrical process vessel, divided in two sections and operating under vacuum, is used in conjunction with two closed pressure filters and a crutcher for supplying a slurry of bleaching earth and a small proportion of the oil. Fig. 61 shows a flow-sheet for the process. The dry neutralized oil is sprayed into the lower section *A* of the evacuated vessel where moisture is flashed off and occluded air removed; this is being assisted by a small amount of "stripping" steam being admitted through sprays at the bottom of this section. The oil has at this stage a temperature of about 50°C and is pumped from the bottom of the section through duplex strainer *B* and an economizer or oil-to-oil heat interchanger *C*, where it is heated by the finished oil. It next passes through a steam heater *D*, where it is heated to the bleaching temperature of about 110°C, to the first pressure filter *E1* which contains semi-spent earth from filtration of oil from the upper section *F* of the process vessel. The residual bleaching power in this earth partially bleaches the oil as it is pumped through. From this first pressure filter the hot partially bleached oil passes, without coming in contact with air, to the upper section *F* of the process vessel, where a small amount of oil-earth slurry, prepared in the crutcher *G* is sprayed in at *H* and is mixed with the hot oil to effect further bleaching. The earth is charged into the crutcher in measured quantities from an earth hopper *I* above while a measured amount of oil is supplied at constant rate from the pipe-line near the economizer. The mixture from *F* is then pumped to the second

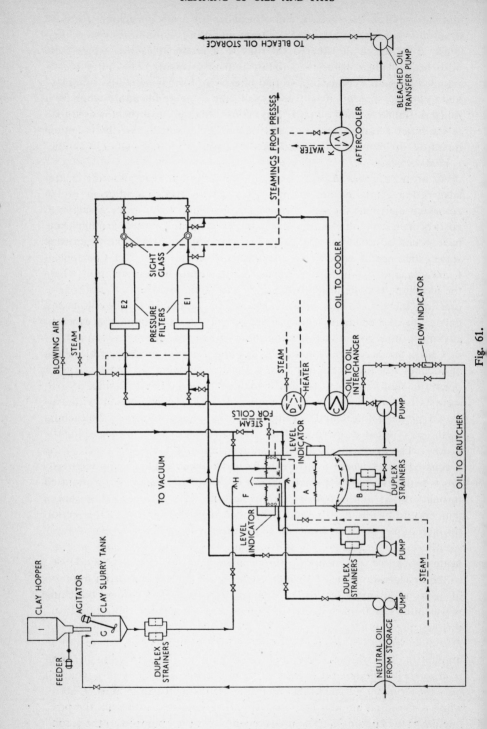

Fig. 61.

pressure filter *E2* for removal of the earth, and the filtered bleached oil passes through the economizer *C* where it heats the de-aerated oil, and a cooler *K* to storage tanks. After a time the second pressure filter will be filled up with filterpress cake; connections are then switched so that this filter becomes the first in the circuit and the first filter is taken out of service for emptying of spent earth and cleaning. During this cleaning period, which is stated to be about half an hour, there is some accumulation of oil in the process vessel, but adequate surge capacity is provided in this vessel to permit the rise in oil level during cleaning.

In this counter-current process, where the unbleached oil with the highest concentration of colouring matter first contacts the semi-spent earth and later, when the concentration is lower, meets fresh earth, the saving in adsorbent is claimed to be 15–20 per cent of that required for batch bleaching, apart from saving in labour. It is reported that this continuous bleaching process can be directly linked up with a continuous neutralization process on oils of constant quality.

Oil Recovery from Bleaching Residue

The amount of fatty matter retained in the filterpress residue after bleaching varies considerably, and may on an average be reckoned to be about 35 per cent; it represents the heaviest item in the cost of bleaching, and it is important to recover as much as possible of it, even though it suffers some degradation in value and quality by the recovery process.

As the fat content of the bleaching residue is often as high as that of many oilseeds, it has sometimes been suggested that the simplest way of recovering the fat would be to mix the residue with the milled oilseed and thus pass it through the crushing or extraction process. There are, however, several objections to this procedure. It would increase the mineral matter content of the oil cake or meal and reduce its value as feeding stuff, or quite spoil it, and statutory regulations prevent in many places this method of disposal. There is also the risk that in addition to the fat various oxidation and other degradation products in the residual oil may cause deterioration in the fresh oil. Furthermore, unless the refinery is combined with an oil mill or oil extraction plant, storage and transportation of the residue causes rapid deterioration of the fatty matter content.

To get the best result of oil recovery from the residue it should be treated as soon as possible after removal from the filterpress. Two methods are principally used:

1. Treatment of the residue at elevated temperature at atmospheric or higher pressures with aqueous solutions of surface-active materials, mostly alkali solutions. Through the lowering of the surface tension and the greater wetting power of these solutions the fat is displaced from its attachment to the adsorbent.

2. Extraction of the filterpress residue with fat solvents.

It has been proposed to make a scouring soap product from the whole residue by saponifying the fatty matter, thus producing a mixture of soap and finely powdered mineral. Salting out of the soap from the mixture has not been found practical.

1. *De-fatting with Surface Active Agents.*—Treatment of fresh bleaching residue with an alkaline solution at boiling temperature and atmospheric pressure permits recovery of a fairly high proportion of the absorbed fat, under good conditions 70–75 per cent. The press residue is mixed in an open tank with an equal quantity of hot water, and while open steam is being blown through from a perforated coil sufficient caustic soda is added to make the lye of 2°Bé strength. After some minutes 10 per cent salt is added and the mixture boiled about 30 mins. At the end of this period three times the amount of hot water is run into the tank and the contents left to settle. The recovered fat is decanted from the surface. The efficiency of the process depends to some extent on the type of adsorbent used for bleaching, and sometimes a mixture of alkali, silicate of soda and soda ash is used with advantage. Wooden vats are preferred to lessen drop of temperature during settling. Activated carbon gives a poor recovery.

In some processes with solutions of surface-active agents the residues are heated under pressure in the presence of neutral electrolytes, such as salt. Fat recovery can also take place at lower temperature if in addition to the alkali there is present a substance more easily wetted by the fat than the bleaching earth. Thus *I. G. Farbenindustrie A.G.* has patented a method[86] by which de-fatting of bleaching earth residue is facilitated by heating with solutions of sulphonic acids, saponin, alkali and other emulsifying compounds in the presence of small quantities of activated carbon.

The quantity and concentration of alkali generally used in these processes does not saponify the fat in the presence of the bleaching earth, as the wetting effect takes preference over saponification. This de-fatting method is principally used in smaller refineries where no solvent extraction plant is available.

A plant frequently used for extraction of bleaching residues with alkali is the autoclave shown in Fig. 62 and made by *Harburger Eisen-und-Bronzewerke A.G.* Germany. To 400 kg filterpress residue are added 400 litre water together with 12 kg soda ash, or the equivalent quantity caustic soda, and 12 kg salt. While the agitator is running, steam of 3 atm. is admitted to the autoclave until a pressure of 3 atm. and a temperature of 135°C is reached. Stirring is continued for some hours with steam blowing through the contents and the blow-off valve open to maintain the pressure. Steaming and stirring is then stopped and the mixture left to settle and separate the fat. The latter is drawn off through a swivel pipe. An emulsion layer of fat and water is taken to a separate tank to recover entrained fat, and the watery sludge from the bottom is run to waste. The recovered fat is often given an acid wash to remove traces of mineral matter, and finally a water-wash to remove acid. By this process the fat content of the spent earth can be reduced to 2–3 per cent. In addition to the autoclave the plant consists of two tanks for alkali and salt, an oil separator, oil tank and means for removal of the sludge (trucks or sludge pump).

Deterioration of the fat absorbed in the adsorbent takes place principally after the press has been opened and the residue exposed to air. Recovery of the fat before this exposure prevents largely deterioration, and such recovery

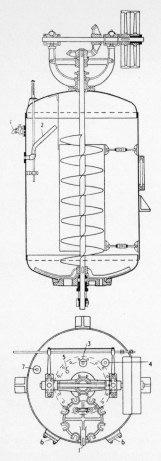

Fig. 62.   Autoclave for de-oiling bleaching earth, according to
Harburger Eisen- und Bronzewerke.

1. Sample cock.
2. Swivel skimmer pipe.
3. Inlet for chemicals.

4. Safety valve.
5. Pressure gauge.
6. Inspection glass.

7. Thermometer.

by washing the press cake with a fat solvent while still in the closed press, which for this purpose must be specially constructed, has been practised for many years. In recent years processes have been successfully developed for displacing the fat in the press cake inside the filterpress by aqueous solutions. This can be done by washing with a hot mild detergent solution, which by its greater wetting power displaces the fat in the adsorbent, though leaving most of the colouring matter and the colloids in the cake. With some bleaching earths hot water alone is effective, but mostly weak alkalis, such as deci-normal caustic soda or carbonate of soda, are used. Immediately the main filtration is finished and oil ceases to flow, the displacement solution is pumped through, air or steam blowing being omitted, and a mixture of aqueous solution and finely dispersed displaced oil issues from the drain-cocks. This mixture can either be left in tanks for separation of the oil, or be passed continuously through centrifugal separators for recovery of the oil, which is almost as good in quality as the bleached oil. The displacement solution can be used again after reheating to near boiling-point. After the washing process the press is steamed for removal of remnants of the displace-ment solution, but these last "runnings" contain only fat of low grade and should be discarded. The press is then ready for opening up and removal of the washed and dried residue.

JAYNES and OSBURN[87] have described a method in which the residue is treated with caustic soda to form with the oil a soap solution corresponding to 4–10 per cent anhydrous soap, which is then separated from the residue in a perforate basket centrifuge. The soap is salted out or the solution treated with acid. A recovery of up to 88 per cent as soap or fatty acids is claimed.

2. *Solvent Extraction of Residues.*—The solvent extraction method for recovery of fat from bleaching residues is more rational, as it gives a higher yield and a better quality of fat than most of those already described, provided that the process is carried out on fresh residues. Steaming of the filterpress should be avoided, as the fat in the damp residue is easily hydrolyzed and the f.f.a. percentage increases markedly. Air blowing should be reduced to a minimum, particularly when filtering semi-drying and drying oils, as these are easily oxidized at the rather high temperatures and dark-coloured inferior fats result. It is better to leave a few per cent more fat in the residue at the end of the filtration than to jeopardize quality by steaming or air blowing, as the solvent will recover 90–95 per cent of the fat.

Suitable types of plant used for solvent extraction of residues, both stationary and rotating cylindrical extractors, are similar to those used for solvent extraction of oil seed, bones, etc. Filterpresses, in which the solvent is pumped through the press cakes, are sometimes used; they must be specially designed to be tight against solvent losses; uniform percolation through the filter beds is, however, difficult to attain. It is preferable, both in stationary and rotating extractors, to use two-stage extraction, the first stage extracting a better quality of oil, while the second stage extract is darker. Where the difference in quality between the two yields is considered less important, the miscella from the second extraction is often used as solvent for the first extraction.

Benzine is the preferred solvent, but where extraction with a non-inflam-mable solvent is required trichlorethylene is mostly used; it is, however, not as specific as benzine, and extracts darker coloured material. The lowest practical temperature should be used in the process to avoid elution of colouring compounds. The residue is allowed to settle at the end of the extraction period and the miscella decanted and filtered.

While it is customary to ascertain the loss of oil in the bleaching process by examining the residue for oil content either by ash determination, calculated on dry adsorbent and dry residue, or by extraction with petrol-ether or other suitable solvent, the control of the efficiency of the solvent extraction process for the de-fatting of residue should preferably be done by analysing the residue before and after extraction by means of the same kind of solvent as used in the process. The solvent used on the plant may have a different selectivity than those generally used for analytical purposes.

Processes have been proposed from time to time for reviving and reactivating the spent extracted bleaching residues; they provide for the complete removal of remnants of fat and similar organic compounds, treatment with superheated steam or heating in kilns to fairly high temperatures. They are of doubtful economical value, and though the reactivated material has adsorptive power towards colouring matters, they are often found to affect unfavourably the ultimate flavour of the fats when used for edible purposes. They can, however, be used on fats and oils for technical purposes.

CHEMICAL BLEACHING METHODS

Chemical bleaching methods are now rarely used on oils and fats intended for edible purposes, as it is better to remove the colouring matter by adsorption than merely to change it by a chemical reaction into a colourless body which is left in the oil. There is also the risk of attack by the chemical on the glycerides, and the flavour always suffers. With the modern activated clays and carbons it is generally possible to obtain equal or better colours than by the various methods suggested for oxidation or reduction bleaches. Chemical bleaching processes are, however, frequently used on fats such as palm oil, bone grease, tallow and fatty acids for technical purposes. The losses of material, arising from retention of fat in the adsorbent and filtration, are largely avoided. In the earlier chapter about purification of fats various treatments with chemicals, for instance, sulphuric acid, have been mentioned, and in course of these purification treatments there is frequently also partial bleaching.

Oxidation Methods.

The most common chemical bleaching method employs some form of mild oxidation of the colouring substance with minimum attack on the glycerides. It is, however, practically impossible to discharge all the colour before the fat itself is attacked by oxidation, the more unsaturated the fat is, the greater the risk. Increase in temperature, light and certain catalysts accelerate the oxidation, which feature is made use of in the manufacture of drying oils.

Although some of the chemicals used are strongly oxidizing, such as peroxides, chromic acid and chlorine, the methods of using them are rather simple and therefore retain some popularity in certain works, but several precautions against excessive treatment are essential, as incorrect procedure may have the opposite effect of that intended, and the result cannot be reversed.

The most common oxidation bleaches are:
1. With atmospheric oxygen, air.
2. Ozone.
3. Peroxides.
4. Light.
5. Dichromate and acid. Permanganate.
6. Chlorine, Hypochlorite.

1. *Bleaching with Atmospheric Oxygen.*—Bleaching by blowing with air is a very old method and is still used frequently on palm oil and tallow. The fat is heated by indirect steam to 100–120°C in tall tanks of wood or a suitable metal to avoid the formation of iron soaps in the crude fat, while a stream of fine air bubbles is dispersed through the fat by means of a system of perforated coils or special air diffusers. The process lasts a few hours, depending on the temperature and air distribution, and is best carried out in a covered tank with ample ventilation to remove the unpleasant acrid smelling vapours. The red components of the colour of palm oil are oxidized more rapidly than the yellow one.

Bleaching of palm oil by air-blowing can be accelerated by adding to the oil small quantities of certain catalysts of the siccative type, such as cobalt or manganese borates or resinates. GEORGI and TEIK[88] and GEORGI and MARSH[89] report intensive bleaching of palm oil at 90°C, when 0·01 per cent cobalt borate or resinate is present, and similar results were obtained with calcium borate.

Dark red palm oil cannot be sufficiently bleached by air-blowing to be satisfactory for white soaps and requires an after bleaching with activated adsorbents. With such oils it is, however, better to rely entirely on bleaching with adsorbents to avoid the risk of oxidation by air, which leads to darkening of the white soaps. These questions have been dealt with by SCHOENFELD[82] and by SCHAEFER and BITTER[90].

2. *Bleaching with Ozone.*—Blowing with ozonized air has been proposed in several patents, but has not been widely employed on industrial scale. In view of the risk of oxidation and the more recently developed highly efficient adsorption methods, it is not likely to play an important part.

3. *Bleaching with Peroxides.*—Hydrogen peroxide in aqueous solution and solutions of certain other peroxides have found some application in special cases. The former is probably the most common and is used occasionally for bleaching tallow, fatty acids, etc., as a solution of 30–40 per cent peroxide content; stronger solutions may damage the fat by overheating as the result of excessive localized oxidation.

Good results have been reported with hydrogen peroxide on such oils as ground nut, sesame, rapeseed and fish oils as well as tallow and, particularly, fatty acids[91]. As the peroxide solution attacks most metals it is recommended to use for the plant such materials as aluminium, stainless steel V2A, enamelled earthenware or iron, and wood[92]. The fat is heated to 50–70°C and stirred with 0·5–2 per cent of the peroxide solution for a few hours; the reaction can be accelerated by being carried out under acid conditions and the addition of about 1 per cent sulphuric acid or glacial acetic acid has been proposed.

Combination of peroxide and adsorption bleaching has been suggested[93]. Tallow and bone grease, otherwise difficult to bleach, are stated to be well bleached after a pre-treatment with dilute sulphuric acid, when agitated 30 mins. with 0·5 per cent of a 30 per cent hydrogen peroxide solution, followed by a mixture of bleaching earth and activated carbon[94].

A similar combination treatment is proposed in a patent by *Lever Brothers & Unilever Ltd.*[95], which describes a bleaching process for tallow and dark-coloured technical fats. These are given a pre-treatment with 0·5–1 per cent of a mixture of equal parts of hydrogen peroxide (30 per cent strength) and commercial phosphoric acid (70–85 per cent strength) at 60–70°C, and after settling and removal of the sludge the pre-treated fat is washed twice with hot water, dried, and subsequently further bleached with 2–6 per cent bleaching earth.

A hydrogen peroxide solution is often used for bleaching the lecithin-oil mixture, obtained in the production of vegetable lecithin from solvent extracted soya bean oil after centrifugal separation of the hydrated sludge.

As is the case with air-bleached fats, those bleached with hydrogen peroxide need no filtration, but it is advisable to wash out thoroughly any excess peroxide solution.

Other peroxides, such as sodium peroxide, calcium peroxide, benzoyl peroxide as well as sodium perborate have been recommended for bleaching of fats, but do not appear to have reached industrial importance.

4. *Bleaching by Light.*—Bleaching of fats by exposure to strong daylight is a very old procedure, but as the bleaching is a light-catalysed oxidation of the colouring matter, it is usually accompanied by some oxidation of the glycerides, and it is not used much nowadays. Fats containing carotenoid compounds, which give them an orange or yellow colour, such as palm oil, butter fat, beef fat, etc., are bleached white when exposed to strong daylight and rapidly develop an unpleasant oxidation flavour. If the fat is kept solid the bleaching proceeds by auto-oxidation from the surface inwards. Where the process is used on solid material such as beeswax, this must be prepared in thin ribbons before exposure to sunlight; when used for liquid oils, these must be exposed in shallow layers. Castor oil for certain purposes where a very white colour is demanded is still bleached by exposure

131

to strong light, when held in layers of a few centimetres depth in large shallow basins of enamelled or tinned metal or in white tiled pans.

5. *Dichromate and Permanganate Bleaching.*—Certain fats are at times bleached by solutions of potassium—or more usually, sodium dichromate—and acid. The reaction between dichromate and acid liberates oxygen which, if the acid used is hydrochloric, reacts with the acid and produces chlorine as additional active agent:

$$Na_2Cr_2O_7 + 4H_2SO_4 = Na_2SO_4 + Cr_2(SO_4)_3 + 4H_2O + 3O$$
$$Na_2Cr_2O_7 + 8HCl = 2CrCl_3 + 4H_2O + 3O$$
$$(2HCl + O = H_2O + Cl_2).$$

The process is carried out in metal tanks, suitably protected against the corrosive effect of the reagents, or in wooden vats, provided with perforated lead coils for admission of steam and air. Oils are treated at ordinary temperature; fats are heated to a few degrees above the melting-point, say 45–50°C, by direct steam through the perforated coil. The required quantity of dichromate, 0·5–2 per cent as a saturated solution in warm water, mixed with dilute sulphuric acid, 25–30 per cent strength, or hydrochloric acid, about 10 per cent strength, is added in slight excess. Agitation is changed from steam to a current of air, which continues till bleaching is finished. A good emulsion should be formed, which is assisted by working at as low a temperature as is consistent with fluidity, and this also has the advantage of preventing the reaction from being too rapid and vigorous.

After addition of the reagents the fats show first a reddish colour which gradually changes via yellow-green to chrome green in ½–1 hour. Soon after agitation is stopped and the contents left to settle. The acid liquor is drawn off, the fat washed with water of about 60°C while agitating with direct steam for 10–15 mins., then left to settle and the wash-water drained away. Washing may be repeated if required.

Dichromate bleaching often gives satisfactory results as regards colour removal. With palm oil it is frequently considered an advantage, when the bleached oil is intended for soap-making, that much of the characteristic violet odour of this oil is retained.

Potassium permanganate reacts in a like manner with sulphuric or hydrochloric acids in liberating oxygen and chlorine and it is used in a similar process; it shows, however, a tendency to leave a brownish tint in the bleached fat, which can be removed by immediate treatment with an aqueous solution of sulphurous acid. This process is not used as much as the dichromate process.

6. *Bleaching with Chlorine Compounds.*—As already mentioned, chlorine takes part in the bleaching process with dichromate or permanganate, if hydrochloric acid is used. It is available more directly when hypochlorites are used for bleaching, which is often the case with tallow. The bleach liquor

is generally prepared from bleaching powder or sodium hypochlorite. For instance, a slurry of bleaching powder ($CaCl_2 + Ca(OCl)_2 + 2 H_2O$) is mixed with soda ash, the precipitated calcium carbonate settled and the resulting sodium hypochlorite solution decanted for use. The bleaching temperature is as a rule lower than in the dichromate process, although it is claimed than when highly concentrated bleaching powder with about 60 per cent available chlorine is used dry, linseed oil can be bleached at 65°C and fatty acids right up to temperatures of about 100°C. The temperature should, however, be low during the addition of the reagent and gradually be increased.

With a sodium hypochlorite solution about 1 per cent is used with an equal amount of hydrochloric acid (33 per cent) or half the quantity of sulphuric acid (33 per cent).

Recently chlorine dioxide, ClO_2, or sodium chlorite, $NaClO_2$, has been produced on industrial scale and used for bleaching dark crude low-grade fats. About 1 per cent of the reagent is added to the fat, which is first mixed with 10 per cent water, and the process is carried out at *ca.* 100°C under acid conditions.

Chlorate in the form of the sodium salt is at times used for bleaching acid oil from acidulation of soapstock. For example, groundnut acid oil is boiled up with steam, and 0·5 per cent sodium chlorate, dissolved in the minimum amount of water, is gradually added, after first adding to the hot oil 1·5–2 per cent sulphuric acid of 25 per cent strength. The addition of chlorate should be spread over $1\frac{1}{2}$–2 hours to avoid too strong a concentration of chloric acid at any time. The process takes about 3 hours, and is carried out in wooden vats. After settling, the acid liquor is drawn off and the bleached oil washed 2 to 3 times with hot water.

Reduction Methods

For bleaching by reduction sodium salts of bisulphite or hydrosulphite are used, the latter well known under the trade name Blankite. Bisulphite is used in acid solution when sulphur dioxide is developed; 1–1·5 per cent in strong solution is mixed into the oil and dilute sulphuric acid gradually added. The hydrosulphite, of which about 0·1 per cent is used, is first diluted with nine volumes of caustic soda solution (6°Bé) and then added to the neutralized fat.

Reduction bleaching is not as effective as oxidation bleaching, and the reduced colour substance may revert in colour when the fat is exposed to air. It is mostly used on fats for soap, and preferably on the soap itself.

Various Chemical Bleaching Methods

In addition to those already mentioned, numerous patents for chemical bleaching methods have been described in the patent literature, but as far as is known few have found practical industrial application. Mention should, however, be made of one which describes a method of overcoming a fault, frequently shown by fats bleached by many of the described methods, or by hydrogenation, namely the development of a pinkish colour when used for white soaps. 0·1–0·3 per cent formaldehyde or paraformaldehyde and 0·1–1 per cent sulphuric acid or bisulphate is added to the fat, which is heated in a vacuum bleacher to 65°C. After an hour's stirring the contents are heated to 100°C, 2 per cent bleaching earth added, agitation continued for 15 mins. and finally calcium carbonate added to neutralize the acid. The fat is cooled and filtered. It is claimed that fats for edible purposes can also be treated by this method[96].

BLEACHING BY HYDROGENATION

It is usual to give oils and fats, intended for hydrogenation, a pre-treatment with an adsorbent of the type used for bleaching; the object is not so much to bleach the oil as to remove extraneous matter which might interfere with hydrogenation efficiency, such as traces of moisture, mucilage, soap, proteins, catalyst poisons, etc. The hydrogenation process itself often has a considerable bleaching effect, partly because the carrier of the catalyst may be an adsorbent for colour, partly because the colouring matters are destroyed or changed by hydrogenation into colourless derivatives. Yellow oils, such as whale oil, cottonseed oil, etc., are changed into white fats. Particularly striking is the change of red or orange palm oil into a white fat. For some edible purposes limited hydrogenation of the oil, but drastic removal of colour of the palm oil is desirable, which is often achieved by the use of a nickel hydrogenation catalyst of limited activity, or by using a mixed catalyst, for example a nickel aluminium catalyst which discharges the palm oil colour, while the iodine value of the fat is reduced by a few units only. As a rule these hydrogenation processes are carried through at 110–180°C and a few atmospheres' pressure.

Where the emphasis is entirely or primarily on bleaching, use is made of the so-called "hydro-bleaching" process recently patented by *Lever Brothers & Unilever Ltd.*[97]. In the manufacture of certain edible fats and shortenings it is often required to obtain maximum bleaching by the combined effect of hydrogen and heat, while at the same time the saturation effect of hydrogen on the unsaturated glycerides should be limited. This is accomplished in the hydro-bleaching process by heating the neutralized oil to 200–220°C at a pressure of 100 atmospheres or more, while a current of hydrogen passes through in the presence of about 0·2 per cent of a catalyst consisting of metallic oxides, for instance, copper and iron oxide, in molar ratio and obtained from co-precipitated hydroxides. If some hydrogenation of the glycerides is desired a small proportion of nickel catalyst, about 0·05 mole or less for each mole of oxide catalyst, is included and co-precipitated; higher proportions lead to more pronounced hardening of the fat. The process takes less than an hour, and hydrogenation of glycerides is highly selective without significant formation of "iso-oleic" acid radicals.

134

Certain precautions have to be observed in preparing the catalyst, and vigorous agitation during hydro-bleaching is essential. After cooling and filtration to remove the catalyst very pale or white fats are obtained. As only 0·2 per cent catalyst is required very little fat is lost in the filterpress cake after bleaching, compared with the proportions lost—or degraded—in the press cake from bleaching with adsorbents.

BLEACHING BY LIQUID-LIQUID EXTRACTION

It was mentioned in connection with liquid-liquid fractionation of fats and the application of that process to de-acidification that it could also be used for removal of colouring matter from fats. The Kellog process, which employs as solvent, propane, which is particularly selective for impurities in fats, including colouring compounds, is now used in several works on a large scale for purifying and bleaching tallow.

BLEACHING BY HEAT

Heating oils in vacuum to relatively high temperatures has often a distinct bleaching effect. It is, however, essential that the oils are first clarified and free from oxidation products and traces of soap. Pre-treated oils, de-acidified by steam distillation in vacuum at 210°C or higher, show a noticeable improvement in colour, and the carotenoid pigments of red or orange palm oil which has been neutralized and has had all traces of soap removed by washing or by adsorption on earth are largely destroyed in the steam deodorization process, if this is carried out at temperatures above 215°C. Complete colour removal is not achieved, but the residual faint yellowish tint is quite suitable for many edible purposes. This method affords considerable savings in bleaching clay and the concomitant losses by oil retention in the filter residue. The heat-bleaching method is less effective on oils in which the pigments include a large proportion of chlorophyll.

Many refiners also take advantage of the extra bleaching effect of higher temperatures by carrying out the vacuum adsorption bleaching of palm oil at 140–160°C, as at such temperatures equally good decoloration is obtained as with a much larger proportion of bleaching earth at the more usual temperatures of 100–110°C.

IV. Deodorization

INTRODUCTION

DEODORIZATION is the process for removing substances which impart undesirable odour and taste to the fat. Some freshly prepared fats have attractive flavours which are valued for edible purposes, for example, butterfat, olive oil, neutral lard, oleo oil, cocoa butter and some cold-pressed vegetable oils, and they are not submitted to deodorization; but most fats and oils, either because of their "natural" flavour or because of changes during storage and processing, need as part of their refining treatment a final deodorization to give them the bland or mild flavour which is considered essential for their successful use in the manufacture of edible fatty products, such as cooking fats, shortenings, margarine and salad oils.

Although de-acidification and bleaching by adsorption generally remove some flavour substances, many of these are strongly soluble in fats and tenaciously retained, and they require a separate deodorization process for their elimination. They may be considered as belonging to the following groups:

1. Substances which are responsible for the characteristic odour and taste of the fats and therefore are present in the fresh fat from un-damaged raw material.
2. Substances arising from deterioration of the fat or the fat-containing raw material through storage, transport and processing, and impurities adventitiously admixed during these stages.

In addition the fats contain certain substances which are inert as regards flavour, such as hydrocarbons, sterols and tocopherols, whose presence is unobjectionable. Part of them is usually removed in the deodorization.

The flavour substances of the first group may be extracted by the fat from the raw material, particularly by hot pressing and solvent extraction. They include unsaturated hydrocarbons, bitter-tasting compounds, carotenoid pigments, terpenes, etc. MARCELET[98] has isolated a number of unsaturated hydrocarbons from olive and ground nut oils, which cause the characteristic flavour of these oils and are not removed by alkali and adsorption treatments. Among the natural flavour compounds may also be mentioned those responsible for the rather pungent flavour of the oils from the "Brassica" group, rapeseed, colza and mustard oils, derived from a glucoside yielding allyl thiocyanate, and the flavouring principle of almond oil.

Investigations of the compounds responsible for the flavour of crude fats have mostly been made on distillation products from the deodorization process, which include in addition to the "natural" flavours also those under group 2, caused by deterioration, as well as compounds formed during the processes of neutralization, bleaching and hydrogenation, and by thermal changes during deodorization. Some compounds, both "natural" and derived from deterioration, are removed in processes prior to deodorization.

The undesirable flavour compounds which remain after the earlier treatments are in practice removed by passing a current of dry steam through the neutralized fat under vacuum, and they are thus concentrated in the distillate. At the same time some of the harmless volatile compounds are removed together with small traces of fatty acids, which may remain after the earlier processes or have been formed by slight hydrolysis during bleaching with acid-activated clay or during deodorization. The glycerides are not volatile under the normal deodorization conditions, as their vapour pressures are very much lower than those of the fatty acids and other volatiles (about 1/1,000), but a small quantity may be carried over by entrainment in the vapours. This is usually less than one promille.

The distillate from deodorization has been examined by various workers as to the nature of the odoriferous compounds. Of the more recent studies may be mentioned those by MARCELET[98], who found in the distillate from olive oil six unsaturated hydrocarbons, which he named Oleatridecen, $C_{13}H_{24}$, B.P. 83–85°C/5 mm, Oleahexadecen, $C_{16}H_{30}$, B.P. 133°C/5 mm, Oleanona-decen, $C_{19}H_{36}$, B.P. 155°C/5 mm, Oleatricosen, $C_{23}H_{42}$, B.P. 205–210°C/5 mm, Oleaoctacosen, $C_{28}H_{50}$, and Oleahexatriaconten, $C_{36}H_{68}$, and two saturated hydrocarbons; Oleatetracosan, $C_{24}H_{50}$, and Oleahexacosan, $C_{26}H_{54}$, which formed solid crystals at room temperature. The presence in oil of none of these compounds was hitherto known. While the saturated hydrocarbons were odourless, the unsaturated ones had a nauseous taste and smell. The total amount of hydrocarbons, calculated on the original quantity of olive oil was only about 0·007 per cent and therefore escaped detection in the original oil.

MARCELET also found in the distillate from ground nut oil two unsaturated hydrocarbons: Hypogaeen, $C_{15}H_{30}$, B.P. 120–125°C/3 mm, and Arachiden, $C_{19}H_{38}$, B.P. 180–185°C/3 mm. Both compounds have a repulsive flavour, and are present in the oil to the extent of 0·002 per cent.

Although only present in such minute proportions, they may be responsible for the characteristic flavour of the two oils. When reintroduced into the deodorized oils they impart to these a close imitation of the crude oils as regards flavours.

Later work by other investigators has shown that there are also other hydrocarbons present in the distillates from different oils, and some of these have undoubtedly been present in the "natural flavours".

Among the odoriferous compounds, formed by degradation of the fats and materials associated with them, are the free fatty acids resulting from hydrolysis of the glycerides. The lower-molecular saturated fatty acids have a very strong odour, particularly butyric acid, isovalerianic acid, caproic acid, etc. Being soluble in water, some of the odour they cause may be eliminated in the neutralization and washing of the crude fats, but some persist through the various treatments and are only removed by deodorization. The highly unsaturated fatty acids from the fats of marine animals, often referred to as "clupanodonic acids", have also a strong specific odour, frequently described as "fishy"; it is partly due to oxidation products from easily oxidizable fatty acids or glycerides containing these, partly to decomposition products of nitrogenous compounds accompanying the fats. The fishy odour is therefore only slightly reduced by neutralization.

Other odoriferous compounds resulting from deterioration of the fat are ketones and aldehydes. HALLER and LASSIEUR[99] reported the presence of several methyl ketones as degradation products of fatty acids in coconut oil and cocoa butter. SALWAY[100] found methyl-nonyl ketone in the volatile odoriferous matter from coconut and palm kernel oils.

JASPERSON and JONES[101] examined the distillates from deodorization of groundnut oil, sunflower oil, cottonseed oil, palm oil, coconut and palm kernel oils and found in the unsaponifiable portion of the first four 0·0135–0·025 per cent (calculated on the original quantity of oil) of terpenes, 0·0045–0·013 per cent of aliphatic hydrocarbons, and 0·0001–0·0008 per cent methyl ketones. From coconut and palm kernel oils they found 0·004 per cent terpene, 0·004 per cent aliphatic hydrocarbons, 0·02–0·026 per cent methyl ketone and 0·002–0·006 per cent of the corresponding carbinols. The whole distillate, including unsaponifiable, fatty acids and entrained glycerides, amounted to 0·1–0·3 per cent of the original fat. The terpenes and the ketones have a very strong odour.

In the distillate may also be found some sterols, fatty alcohols from hydrogenation, tocopherols and other inhibitols, and substances about which little is known at present. Iron soaps have frequently been reported; they arise probably from the attack of fatty acid vapour on steel plant.

Other degradation products, such as carbohydrates, protein and phosphatide derivatives, etc., are largely removed in processes prior to deodorization.

Certain flavours, picked up by the fat during treatment, for example "burnt" flavours from overheating of seed during crushing, traces of solvent from extraction, "earthy" and bitter flavours from adsorbents for bleaching, "hardening" flavour from hydrogenation, etc., require deodorization for their removal. Peroxides formed by mild oxidation of the fat during processing are also removed in deodorization.

Most of the odoriferous compounds have vapour pressures of similar order as those of the fatty acids, and are therefore removed in steam distillation together with the acids.

The loss of part of the "natural" antioxidants or inhibitols by steam deodorization may leave the fat more susceptible to attack by oxidation, specially if some of these compounds have been exhausted through incipient oxidation and deterioration of the fat prior to refining, but from good quality crude fats deodorization yields a very stable product.

THE THEORETICAL BASIS FOR DEODORIZATION

Deodorization, in practice, is the removal of the odoriferous matter by distillation in a current of steam in vacuum and at elevated temperatures (150–250°C). Under these conditions neutral fat is not volatile. The vapour pressure of the odoriferous compounds is so low that very high temperature would be required to distil them off at atmospheric pressure; hence the need of a good vacuum and a current of inert gas to reduce the distillation temperature below that at which damage or decomposition of the neutral fat might take place. Of the inert gases dry steam is the most suitable because of its cheapness, its high specific volume, and the comparative ease with which it can be condensed and removed from the system; a non-condensible inert gas would require very elaborate and expensive pumping machinery for removal and recovery.

Deodorization is therefore essentially a distillation in a current of steam and governed largely by the principles and laws of that process. It also removes such small quantities of free fatty acids that may have been formed in the fat after neutralization, for instance, as the result of bleaching with acid-activated earth, or in the hydrogenation process.

There are no complete data about the odoriferous compounds that have to be removed, and their vapour pressures, but an approximate indication is given by the boiling-points of the methyl ketones, which have been identified and which range from 193–263°C at atmospheric pressure. The methyl-nonyl ketone of palm kernel oil has a vapour pressure of about 230 mm mercury at 160°C, and if present to the extent of 0·2 per cent would have at 160°C a vapour pressure of about 0·5 mm.

An indication of the lowering of the boiling points of fatty acids when distilled in a current of different proportions of steam is shown by the following figures:

Ratio steam: fatty acid	2·5:1	1:1
Lauric acid	191°C	215°C
Myristic acid	211°C	235°C
Palmitic acid	224°C	248°C
Stearic acid	243°C	265°C
Oleic acid	239°C	262°C

Without a current of steam the boiling-points of the fatty acids at atmospheric pressure would be so high that decomposition of the fat would occur. At 16 mm abs. pressure the boiling-points of the principal saturated acids concerned (from lauric acid to stearic acid) range from 182°C to 240°C.

The table below gives the temperatures at which a number of mixed fatty acids distil at pressures of 5–8 mm.

Groundnut oil fatty acids	210–220°C
Soya bean oil „	210–220°C
Cottonseed oil „	215–225°C
Olive oil „	210–220°C
Coconut oil „	200–210°C
Palm oil „	210–215°C

SCHOENFELD[102] gives the distillation temperatures of mixed fatty acids from the same oils at 20 mm pressure, average and maximum temperatures:

Groundnut oil fatty acids	230–240°C
Soya bean oil „	230–245°C
Cottonseed oil „	235–250°C
Olive oil „	230–240°C
Coconut oil „	215–230°C
Palm oil „	225–235°C

The vapour pressures of the various components in the deodorizer charge conform to DALTON's law of partial pressures, and the total pressure is the sum of all the individual partial pressures. By passing a current of steam—the so-called "open", "direct" or "stripping" steam—into the fat in the deodorizer, distilling commences, when the combined pressures of the steam and the volatile components reach the pressure on the surface of the fat, and therefore at lower temperature than without steam. The lower that pressure—the operating pressure—is, the lower the temperature of distillation; hence the importance of a good vacuum.

The volatile components distil in such ratios that their molar proportions in the vapour correspond to their partial pressures. If W_a is the weight of component A in the vapour, and W_b the weight of a second component B in the vapour, p_a and p_b the corresponding partial pressures, and M_a and M_b the molecular weights of the components, the ratio of the vapour volumes of A and B equals the ratio of their partial pressures $p_a{:}p_b$, and as the weights of equal volumes of A and B at same temperature and pressure is proportional to their molecular weights M_a and M_b, the ratio of the weights of the two components in the vapour is—

$$\frac{W_a}{W_b} = \frac{p_a \cdot M_a}{p_b \cdot M_b}.$$

There is a number of different constructions of deodorizers, which will be described later. They are generally cylindrical metal vessels, provided with means for indirect heating of the fat to a suitable operating temperature, and with a distributor for injecting into the fat open steam for distilling or "stripping" off the volatile substances. Connections to an efficient vacuum and condensing system for the distillate are also provided.

While the removal of existing volatile and odoriferous components takes place, some slight formation of free fatty acids by hydrolysis of neutral glycerides from the action of steam and high temperature may occur at the same time, but this is largely prevented by high vacuum. In batch deodorization, however, there may, owing to the height of the fat charge, be a hydraulic pressure at the bottom of the vessel, where the open steam enters, corresponding to 150–200 mm mercury, and this, together with high deodorization temperature, increases the risk of slight hydrolysis and formation of free fatty acids, even at low absolute pressures on the surface of the fat.

There is also in some cases evidence of the formation of some new odoriferous compounds as the result of heat-decomposition of existing compounds. These, as well as any free fatty acids formed during deodorization, can be eliminated when the process is operated under correct conditions.

To obtain these correct conditions in an efficient and economical manner a number of points must be considered, such as temperature, the amount of open steam, its distribution, the vacuum, etc.

As an increase in temperature increases the vapour pressure of the volatile components, it is obviously advantageous to operate at as high a temperature as is practical. The relationship, according to the Clausius-Clapeyron law, is that the logarithm of the vapour pressure is proportional to the absolute temperature (T), hence a moderate increase in temperature will give a considerable increase in vapour pressure and thus in volatility. POOL and RALSTON have shown an example of this[103] when giving the vapour pressures of palmitic acid at different temperatures:

177°C	.	1·8 mm.	232°C	.	25·0 mm.
204°C	.	7·4 mm.	260°C	.	72·0 mm.

There are, however, reasons for not going too far in increasing the temperatures, as higher temperatures increase the risk of hydrolysis of glycerides with formation of free fatty acids and thereby higher process losses. Furthermore, at temperatures above 190–200°C the effect of the metal used for constructing the deodorizer must be considered; steel may give a metal flavour to the fat, and special metals such as stainless steel or nickel are recommended. Finally, at temperatures above 200°C there is the possibility of some molecular rearrangement of the glycerides, particularly the more unsaturated ones. Hydrogenated fats, where fatty acid radicals more unsaturated than oleic acid have largely been eliminated, can therefore be deodorized at higher temperatures than liquid oils.

It should also be remembered that although glycerides are generally considered non-volatile under most deodorizing conditions, the combination of high temperatures—225°C and upwards—and low pressures—10 mm and lower—may cause a small loss of neutral glycerides, particularly if these are rich in lauric and myristic acid radicals (the coconut oil group).

With regard to the amount of steam required it has already been mentioned that the use of open steam is to effect the vaporization of the volatile components at a lower temperature. The bubbles of steam rise through the liquid fat and become charged with volatile components in a concentration depending on the partial vapour pressures of these components. The partial pressure of a component in the steam emerging from the deodorizer is sometimes less than the partial pressure which represents equilibrium with the volatile component in the fat. The vaporization efficiency E is therefore defined as the ratio of the actual partial pressure of the volatile components in the steam (p_{vs}) to the partial pressure of the volatile components which would be in equilibrium with the fat (p_{vf}). E has been found to be a function of the nature of the volatile components, the distance the steam bubble travels through the fat and the size of the individual bubbles. It is expressed in the equation (7)[104]:

$$E = \frac{p_{vs}}{p_{vf}} = 1 - e^{-K\frac{L}{D}}$$

where E, p_{vs} and p_{vf} are as already defined, e is the base of Naperian logarithms, L is the depth of the fat through which the steam bubbles rise, D the diameter of the bubbles and K a constant characteristic of the volatile component and determined by its diffusion rate in the vapour state.

To obtain a high vaporization efficiency the open steam should be injected into the fat in the deodorizer through a system of fine holes to provide a large number of small bubbles with a large total surface relative to the weight. For practical reasons holes in metal coils, pipes or boxes are rarely less than 3 mm, but special ceramic diffusion plates are sometimes used. Their practical value seems, however, doubtful in batch deodorizers, where the open steam is injected at the bottom of a column of oil several feet high, and the pressure exerted by the column and the large relative surface of the bubbles create good conditions for a high vaporization efficiency. With the gradual expansion of the bubbles rising through the column under rapidly diminishing pressure, and consequently reduction in bubble surface relative to the volume, there might be a tendency for the vaporization efficiency to fall towards the surface. Some refiners prefer therefore to introduce part of the steam by an auxiliary injection system at a suitable level nearer the surface.

In practice it has been found that within the range of absolute pressures used in deodorization the saturation of the steam with volatile components is fairly rapid, and the vaporization efficiency in batch deodorizers and correctly dimensioned continuous deodorization columns is generally of the order of 0.75–0.9, and often 1.0.

The amount of steam required for deodorization depends on a number of factors: the size of the charge, the temperature, the vacuum, the nature of the volatile compounds, their vapour pressure, etc. Theoretical studies of this subject and the application of the physical laws of gases and solutions to the features involved in deodorization was a sequence to the mathematical treatment originally evolved in connection with analogous processes in the petroleum industry; its application to deodorization of edible fats has been described in papers by BRASH[105], SINGER[106], BAILEY[107], BATES [108] and others. It must however be recognized that oils and fats vary considerably in their response to the theory owing to variations in their composition and the diversity in type and quantity of the volatile components; furthermore, deodorization is not a clear-cut steam distillation of compounds of standard composition; other features play a part, as will be described later. Application of the theory does, however, afford a guide to the factors which play an important part in the efficiency and economy of the process.

An indication of the moles of steam (M_s) needed can be obtained from the following consideration:

Within the temperature range of deodorization the substances concerned generally comply with RAOULT's law, i.e., the ratio of the vapour pressure of a volatile component in dilution in the fat (p_{vf}) to the vapour of the pure volatile component (P_v) is equal to the molar fraction of it in the fat:

$$\frac{p_{vf}}{P_v} = \frac{\text{moles of volatile component } (M_v)}{\text{moles fat } (M_f) + \text{moles volatile comp. } (M_v)}.$$

As M_v is very small compared with M_f it is approximately right to use the equation:

$$\frac{p_{vf}}{P_v} = \frac{M_v}{M_f}.$$

In the vapour from the deodorizer, steam and volatile compounds from the fat will at any time be present in a molar ratio equal to the ratio of their partial vapour pressures, i.e.,

$$\frac{dM_s}{dM_v} = \frac{p_s}{p_{vs}},$$

where p_s is the partial pressure of the steam, p_{vs} the partial pressure of the volatile component in the vapour mixture. P_o is the total pressure in the vapour and equals $p_s + p_{vs}$, and is the same as the operating pressure in the vacuum above the fat. As p_{vs} is very small compared with p_s the latter approximates closely to P_o and the equation may be written as—

$$\frac{dM_s}{dM_v} = \frac{P_o}{p_{vs}}. \qquad \cdot \qquad \cdot \qquad \cdot \qquad \cdot \qquad \cdot \qquad (1)$$

As the vaporization efficiency E has been defined as $p_{vs}{:}p_{vf}$, and as it has been shown with approximation from RAOULT's law that $p_{vf} = \dfrac{M_v \cdot P_v}{M_f}$ the insertion of the value of p_{vf} into the equation

$$E = \frac{p_{vs}}{p_{vf}}$$

will give

$$E = \frac{p_{vs} \cdot M_f}{M_v \cdot P_v}$$

or

$$p_{vs} = \frac{E \cdot M_v \cdot P_v}{M_f} \qquad \cdot \qquad \cdot \qquad \cdot \qquad \cdot \qquad (2)$$

Inserting into equation (1) the value of p_{vs} from equation (2) will give the following equation:

$$\frac{dM_s}{dM_v} = \frac{P_o}{\dfrac{E \cdot M_v \cdot P_v}{M_f}} = \frac{P_o \cdot M_f}{E \cdot M_v \cdot P_v}.$$

By integration this gives—

$$M_s = \frac{P_o \cdot M_f}{E \cdot P_v} \cdot l_n \frac{M_{v1}}{M_{v2}},$$

where M_{v1} and M_{v2} are initial and final concentrations of volatile components in the fat.

This equation shows the factors which affect steam economy. The amount of steam required increases with increase in the fat charge (M_f), with increase in the operating pressure P_o (less good vacuum), and with fall in the vaporization efficiency E. It also increases with the degree of elimination of volatile compounds from the fat ($M_{v1} - M_{v2}$), and is the higher the lower is the vapour pressure P_v or volatility of the pure volatile component in the fat.

The equation also shows that as the amount of fat M_f and the vapour pressure P_v of the pure volatile components in a particular charge may be regarded as constant, when working at constant deodorizing temperature, and if E is kept approximately constant, a reduction in operating pressure P_o, which connotes an increase in the volume of the steam, effects a considerable economy in steam consumption. Or if the same weight of steam is injected at lower operating pressure, the increased volume will ensure completion of the process in shorter time.

It is therefore evident that the efficiency of the removal of volatile components depends on the volume of the steam in relation to the volume of the fat, and in theory it is immaterial whether the volume of steam is passed through the fat in a shorter or longer time, as long as the temperature is kept constant. The advantage of the low operating pressure is that a certain volume of steam is passed through in a shorter time. This has been borne out in practice by following the removal during deodorization of indicator compounds such as free fatty acids, or chromogenic compounds such as sesamol, the removal of which runs parallel with that of the odoriferous substances. It has been shown that most of the volatile components are removed fairly rapidly, depending to some extent on the quality of the crude fat and the pre-treatment prior to deodorization, but relatively more steam is required for removal of the last fraction of the volatiles to obtain a stable and satisfactory product.

The rate at which the required volume of steam is passed through the fat is, however, limited for several reasons. The mass-velocity of the vapour and violent ebullition of the steam may cause the stream of vapours to carry upwards a mist of droplets of fat, and this force may, when the particles are below a certain size, overcome the force of gravity and prevent the droplets from falling back. It has been shown by SOUDERS and BROWN[109] that entrainment losses are determined by the velocity and density of the steam and by the diameter of the particles. The velocity which will keep particles in suspension is—

$$V = \sqrt{\frac{2g \; D \; (d_1 - d_2)}{3 \; kd_2}}.$$

k is an empirical constant and g the acceleration due to gravity. The equation can therefore be written as—

$$V = K \sqrt{\frac{D \; (d_1 - d_2)}{d_2}},$$

where D is the diameter of the particle, d_1 and d_2 the densities of the fat particles and the vapour respectively. Hence the greater the velocity of the steam the larger the droplets that can be carried along, temperature and operating vacuum being constant. This loss can be minimized by having in the deodorizer a good headspace and an efficient baffling arrangement to trap droplets. In good equipment and with an adequate rate of steaming this loss should be less than one promille.

The theoretical considerations show that it is most economical in steam to operate at low absolute pressures; a good vacuum and a suitable high temperature shorten the time required for distilling off the odoriferous components. It is, however, the opinion of many refiners that deodorization should not be reduced below a certain minimum time, as some odoriferous substances, largely unknown, are formed during the process and their formation is connected with a time factor. Unless this process is completed during the deodorization and the compounds thus formed are distilled off, the fat, although apparently satisfactory in quality immediately after deodorization, may revert in flavour in course of time and show lack of stability. This development of odoriferous compounds, which is fairly rapid at the high temperature of deodorization, proceeds nevertheless slowly at ordinary temperature, unless completed in course of the deodorization. For that reason it is often advisable to arrange the period of high temperature treatment to cover at least several hours, depending on the deodorization temperature. In some continuous plants, built on the tower principle with plates and bubble caps, where the steaming time is rather short, pre-heaters are provided for keeping the charge near deodorization temperature for about an hour to effect the heat reaction while just sufficient steam bubbles through for agitation. In batch deodorizers where the vapour tension of the steam at the bottom of the vessel is many times higher than at the surface the reaction takes place at the lower levels, and its completion is assisted by efficient circulation of the fat by suitable arrangements of the steam inlets. This will also help to maintain a high vaporization efficiency, which can often be promoted by auxiliary injection of steam at a higher level, as mentioned earlier.

The need for this pyrolytic change varies with the quality of the fats and is less important with hydrogenated fats, as they have already during hydrogenation been submitted to high temperature treatment for some hours.

Although the theoretical basis for deodorization indicates the factors and conditions which affect the economy and efficiency of the process, it can only be used as a guide, as the fats vary in composition, and even after pre-treatment, neutralization and decoloration vary in quality and content of odoriferous and volatile compounds. Each type and consignment of fat presents therefore a specific problem, and temperature, rate of steaming and duration of the process or, in the case of continuous or semi-continuous plants, rate of through-flow, must be assessed largely on the basis of experience with the plant available.

The two important criteria for performance evaluation of deodorizing are quality and economy.

There is no scientific way of assessing quality. While the small amount of free fatty acids left in the fat after deodorization can be determined analytically, it has in most cases little influence on quality, as long as it is below 0·1 per cent, and it is with good plant generally less than 0·05 per cent. Accelerated stability tests, based on resistance to peroxide formation or to deterioration when exposed to heat, are frequently applied, but fats can pass these tests well and still be unsatisfactory in flavour. The judgment of flavour quality is therefore a matter of experience by skilled operators, and the standards vary from place to place, and to some extent also with the purpose for which the deodorized fat is to be used.

The question of economy, provided the distillation and entrainment losses are kept within the usual 0·2–0·4 per cent is largely a matter of heat and steam requirements, which again depend on deodorization temperature and vacuum. The heat needed for warming the fat to, and keeping it at, deodorization temperature may be supplied as indirect steam, if this is available at sufficiently high pressure for the temperature required. If not, circulation of superheated water, hot mineral oil or Dowtherm vapour are efficient methods. In some refineries where the boiler steam is not hot enough to reach the peak temperature for deodorization, electrical immersion heaters are used as auxiliary means of heating. The amount of heat required for this purpose depends, of course, on the temperature of the fat before reaching the deodorizing equipment, but otherwise there is not much difference between the various methods, although plant arrangements may cause minor differences.

The amount of steam required as direct or stripping steam depends on the volume and hence on the vacuum, which again depends on the temperature of the cooling water in the condensers. Where steam jet thermo-compressors are used as vacuum augmentors, more steam—2–4 times as much—is used for that purpose than for stripping, but the combined quantity is usually less than if working without augmentors and relying on cooling water of about 15°C in the condensers for sustaining the vacuum. The quantity of stripping steam, when deodorizing at about 6 mm absolute pressure, is of the order of 4–6 per cent of the weight of the fat.

While previously superheated steam was generally used for stripping, this is now rarely the case. It does not contribute significantly to the heating, and may cause local overheating of the fat. Boiler steam from de-aerated water, throttled down to about 2 atmospheres pressure, is now mostly used as direct steam, and by passing it through an orifice plate with suitably placed valves and pressure gauge the steam flow can be controlled and measured.

146

DEODORIZATION PLANT

A deodorization plant consists of the following units:

1. The deodorization vessel and auxiliary plant such as vapour traps and coolers.
2. Plant for production of vacuum and condensation of vapours.

There are a number of different arrangements of the actual deodorization vessel and its auxiliary equipment for heating, steaming and cooling the charge, and the process can be conducted as (a) a batch process, (b) a continuous process, (c) a semi-continuous process.

Some features are common to all types of plant. The deodorizers are cylindrical with shallow dished top and bottom or, if horizontal, dished ends. All joints are welded to keep the vessel completely airtight, and this is well insulated to minimize radiation losses. Where deodorization temperatures are below 200°C the vessel is usually made of carbon steel; where the process is regularly carried through at higher temperatures, quality considerations make it desirable to use stainless steel or nickel, or steel clad with these metals. Fittings containing copper or copper alloys should be shunned.

Means should be provided for charging the vessel rapidly with the desired quantity of fat and for bringing this to the required temperature. This can be done either inside or outside the vessel, in accordance with its design, but the fat should be under vacuum when above 60–70°C and be de-aerated before reaching the temperature of deodorization. An efficient system for distributing the direct steam is essential as already referred to, partly to attain high vaporization efficiency, partly to ensure thorough circulation and heat transfer to the fat charge. Pipes warmer than the fat should be fully submerged in the fat charge as droplets splashing on to exposed pipes might get overheated. A good baffling and trapping system will mimimize entrainment losses, but should not trap and throw back the compounds the process is designed to remove. A sampling cock for withdrawing and cooling samples out of contact with air is essential for showing progress of the deodorization. After the process the fat should be cooled to 60°C or below under vacuum or out of contact with air. This cooling can be done inside the deodorizer by a set of cooling coils for water, which can be the same as the heating coils if steam is used for heating. Some designers of plant prefer to cool the fat in separate coolers. By an appropriate system of heat-interchangers much of the heat in the steam used for heating and keeping the fat at deodorization temperature and in the water used for cooling the fat after the process can be recovered with considerable effect on the total heat economy.

Batch Deodorizers

Various constructions are used. When of the vertical cylindrical type the height is usually about twice the diameter and the working capacity slightly more than half the volume to provide ample head-space for expansion of the charge, when heated up, and for ebullition and splashing, thus avoiding excessive entrainment losses. An amply dimensioned vapour-offtake at the top connects with the vacuum system, and a baffle plate is usually provided to prevent entrained particles being carried by the vapour stream straight into the offtake.

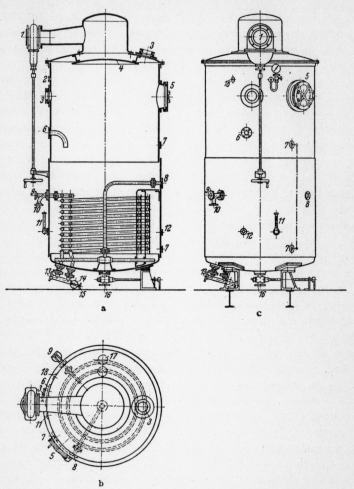

Fig. 63.   Deodoriser, according to *Harburger Eisen- und Bronzewerke.*

Fig. 63 shows a typical vertical batch deodorizer. The fat-inlet *6* is at the side, a little above the level of the contents. As the vessel is under vacuum while being filled some de-aeration of the fat occurs during this operation. The outlet for vapours and the connection to the vacuum and condensation system is at *1* with baffleplate *4*. At the bottom of the vessel is the distributor for direct steam, in this case in the form of a star or "spider" of perforated pipes, supplied from a central steam box. The perforations are in the side of the pipes to improve circulation and mixing of steam and fat; the inlet to the distributor is at *8*. The fat is heated and kept at deodorization temperature by a coil system for indirect steam *9, 14*, which, if the fat has not been pre-heated before reaching the deodorizer, should be dimensioned to permit fairly rapid heating of the contents to operating temperature. The same pipe system can be used for circulating cold water for cooling the fat in vacuum after deodorization *10, 13*. To avoid incrustation in the coils soft water should be used for cooling. The deodorizer is provided with sight glasses with illumination *3*, level gauge *7*, thermometer *11*, sampling cock for drawing and cooling samples under vacuum *12*, vent *18*, pressure gauge *2*, etc. and with valves for inlet *6*, outlet *16*, and connection to vacuum *1*, all specially designed for tightness against high vacuum. The vessel has welded joints and is protected against heat losses by efficient insulation.

In the deodorizer in Fig. 64 certain differences in detail have been introduced. Instead of the conventional convex dished top a concave structure is used, so that any condensate of volatile compounds on the top can flow towards the centre of the cover and drip into the outlet funnel for the vapour offtake, which is carried horizontally or with a slight down-gradient towards and through the side wall to the connection to a trap and to the vacuum system. The heating coils for indirect steam form a triple cylindrical nest of helical coils connected with common top and bottom headers. The direct steam supply consists of a double system, of which one with inlet at *A* supplies steam for stripping via a perforated circular coil at the bottom, whereas the other with inlet at *B* injects steam into a central surge tube for improving the circulation of the fat by forcing it up through the open vertical central tube against the umbrella-shaped dome above, from which it is sprayed out towards the periphery.

The deodorizer shown in section in Fig. 65 has the inlet pipe in the upper part of the cylindrical shell and the oil is delivered as a stream against the wall, which facilitates de-aeration during filling under vacuum. The vapour offtake or "fume pipe" is through the side with a slight slope towards a fat-trap (not shown). Sight and light-glasses in the cover permit observation of the process. Indirect steam for heating to and maintenance of deodorization temperature is supplied through a set of six helical coils connecting circular headers; the large surface provided by these coils of relatively small bore increases the rate of heat transfer and accelerates heating of the contents. The same coil system is also used for cooling the oil with water after the process. There is a dual supply system of direct steam for stripping, one supply leading to a distribution box fitted with radial perforated pipes (spider) at the bottom, another to a perforated circular pipe, fitted a short distance below the oil surface, to give an auxiliary supply of stripping steam (see p. 142).

In the deodorizers described the temperature has been reached and maintained by means of steam, which is usually available in refineries of sufficient pressure to ensure that the process can be carried out at 170–190°C, which are the common temperatures in Europe. Where, as in U.S.A., deodorization, particularly of hydrogenated fat, is done at higher temperatures—220–250°C—high-pressure steam or other means of heating are adopted,

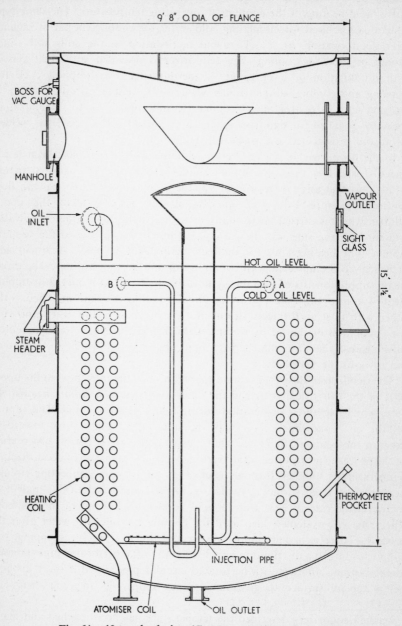

Fig. 64.   12-ton deodorizer (Courtesy: *Bamag Ltd., London*).

for instance special mineral oil or Dowtherm vapour. Fig. 66 shows a diagram and flow sheet of a deodorizer plant for batch operation in which Dowtherm is used for indirect heating of the fat and for drying and superheating the stripping steam.

Dowtherm, which has been widely employed in industry for heating in

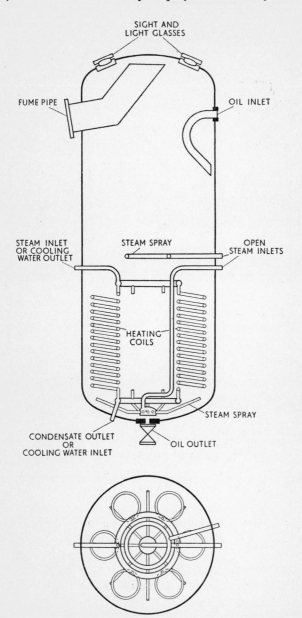

Fig. 65. Deodorizer (Courtesy: *W. J. Fraser & Co. Ltd., Dagenham*).

recent years, is an eutectic mixture of diphenyl and diphenyloxide, the ratio being 26·5–73·5 per cent. It melts at 12°C and boils at atm. pressure at 258°C, i.e., a very suitable temperature for heating oil to the higher deodorization temperatures; the closed Dowtherm heating system can therefore be used at atmospheric or slightly higher pressures; the heat transfer area of coils must, however, be larger than when steam is used, as the latent heat

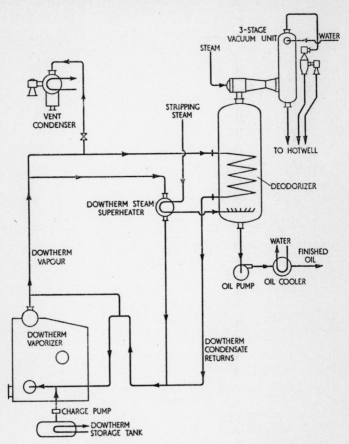

Fig. 66.   Diagram of batch deodorizer with Dowtherm heating
(Courtesy: *Foster-Wheeler Corporation, London*).

of Dowtherm vapour is relatively low[110]. Fig. 66 indicates the Dowtherm heating system, consisting of the vaporizer, preferably heated with gas or oil, the vapour pipes supplying heat to the coil in the deodorizer and to the superheater for stripping steam, and the return pipes for condensed vapour taking the Dowtherm back to the vaporizer. In suitable locations this circulation can be by gravity.

The deodorizer is operating under an absolute pressure of 4–6 mm, maintained by a 3-stage vacuum unit consisting of vacuum augmentor and 2-stage steam ejector. At this vacuum and at 215–220°C the process takes 4–4½ hours. In this plant the cooling of the deodorized oil takes place in a separate tubular cooler, but vessels are also used in which there are coil systems for Dowtherm and for indirect steam as additional source of heat; the latter coils can then also be used for water for partial cooling of the finished oil. In some plants the heating system is outside the deodorizer, in which case

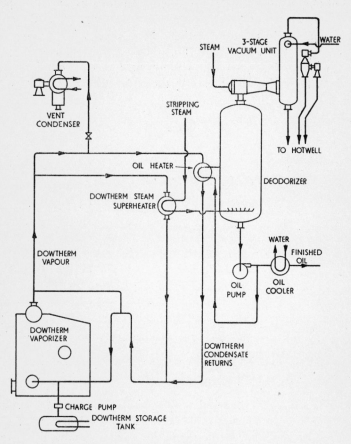

Fig. 67.   Diagram of batch deodorizer with external heating
(Courtesy: *Foster-Wheeler Corporation, London*).

the contents, while being heated to operating temperature and during deodorization, are continuously circulated by a pump from the deodorizer through a tubular heater and back; the only inside coil is for stripping steam (Fig. 67).

In some deodorizers the coils for indirect steam form one or two rings of vertical pipes connecting upper and lower headers, and to increase the heat transfer surface the vertical pipes are at times provided with longitudinal fins protruding a distance about equal to the bore of the pipe. It has

153

been stated that this system interferes little with the rise of the steam bubbles from the stripping steam distributor and with the release of volatiles.

A feature which is emphasized in certain plants is the use of distilled water for generating the steam for stripping to avoid the possibility of imparting foreign flavours to the oil in the deodorizer from material used for water treatment in the boilers.

In the technical and patent literature many deodorizers for batch operation are described, which vary in constructional details though working on the principles outlined in previous sections. Most of them are of the vertical cylindrical type, but occasionally horizontal cylinders are used. Fig. 68 shows a diagram of such a vessel which in practice has been found to give good results. The circulation caused by the direct steam is stated to be good,

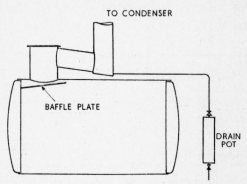

Fig. 68.   Sketch of horizontal deodorizer.

the surface relative to the height of the contents is large and the entrainment losses small. It is, however, doubtful whether the vaporization efficiency is as high as in the vertical type.

Continuous Deodorizers

These are mostly tall cylindrical towers with a number of superimposed plates provided with bubble caps or other means for distributing the steam in each section, and with overflow pipes or dams to enable the fat to flow from section to section from the top downwards in counter-current to the direct steam, which is injected through a perforated pipe near the bottom and ascends through the holes in the plates, bubbling through the shallow layers of fat on the plates, until it reaches the vapour-offtake at the top which connects to the vacuum. The fat enters the pre-evacuated column, and while descending from plate to plate presents a large surface to the action of the steam that carries away the volatile components. In some cases pre-heaters are built into the top of the column as a separate compartment.

In a column deodorizer made by *Etablissements A. Olier*, France, the upper part of the column operates under the vacuum controlled by the temperature of the condenser water, while in the lower part the vacuum is increased by a steam ejector discharging into the upper half. This system lessens the drop in vacuum between the bottom and top of the column.

An advantage claimed for the continuous column plants is the short time the fat is exposed to the high deodorization temperature, as the through-run only takes a few minutes, and that therefore higher temperatures are permissible than in batch plants. Furthermore, that owing to the shallow layers of fat on the plates a smaller difference in vacuum is possible between top and bottom of the plant, and consequently a better utilization of the direct steam with concomitant economy in production of vacuum and in water consumption for condensation. These plants are most suitable for protracted runs on fats of regular quality, particularly hydrogenated fats, where the short period of steaming may suffice. Where change in quality and type of fat is frequent, and where a longer exposure to deodorization temperature is considered essential, regulation of the through-flow presents at times difficulties, and some plants are therefore provided with a post-deodorizer, where a short final deodorization is given on the batch system, or with a pre-treatment vessel where the fat is kept at deodorization temperature while a small quantity of direct steam is passed through for agitation; the final deodorization is then done in the continuous column. The deodorized oil leaving the column thus comes in contact with fresh direct steam only.

For table and salad oils, where it is often desirable to retain some of the original flavour of the fresh oil, continuous plants are less suited.

Deodorization columns are provided with separate tubular coolers, which can deal with the continuous flow of fat and cool it to below 60°C before exposure to air.

One of the earlier designs of a plant for continuous deodorization, as patented by BOLLMANN[111], is shown in Fig. 69. The tower is fitted with a number of dividing floors 2, 3, 4, 5 with central tube passages for direct steam and vapours 6. These tubes are covered with loose conical caps 7, which deflect and distribute the ascending steam through the fat which flows in counter-current over Raschig rings, used as packing between the floors. A layer of fat collects on each intermediate floor, where it is heated by indirect steam in coils 8 and overflows through pipes 9 into the compartment below. The indirect heating steam enters the column at 19 and leaves at 20. The fat inlet is at 10, outlet at 11. Direct steam for stripping is supplied through the perforated distributor pipe 12. An auxiliary heating pipe for indirect steam is fitted at 13. The vapour outlet 14 at the top connects with the vacuum and condensation plant. The column in this plant was used as a pre-deodorizer, the steamed fat being taken via the outlet 11 and the constant-level tank 15 to vessel 16, where it was given a further heat treatment in vacuum, and finally cooled to a suitable temperature in coil 17 before exposure to air.

This early type of plant has been followed by many improvements. Some towers have a large number of perforated division trays, each fitted with an overflow pipe leading to an oil seal on the plate below and regulating the depth of the layers on the plates. The current of steam rises through the fine holes, practically preventing the fat from draining through, thereby maintaining the shallow layers of fat on the plates to the level of the overflow. For these plants the fat is pre-heated to deodorization temperature and after treatment passed through a tubular cooler.

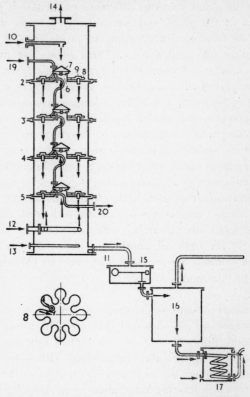

Fig. 69. Continuous deodorizer, according to H. Bollmann.

The continuous deodorization columns have found their widest application in America. An example of a modern plant is the Foster-Wheeler continuous deodorizer shown diagrammatically in Fig. 70.

The plant consists of a de-aerator, a heat-exchanger for heating the incoming fat by the deodorized fat, a heater for bringing the fat up to deodorization temperature, a deodorization column containing 10–12 superimposed trays fitted with bubble caps and an overflow dam, a pump for removing the deodorized fat from the bottom of the column through the heat-exchanger, and a tubular cooler for the final cooling of the fat against water. A vacuum augmentor or booster ejector and a barometric jet condenser with 2-stage steam jet ejectors keeps the plant under high vacuum. Stainless steel is used for construction where fat is in contact with metal.

The incoming charge is first de-aerated by cascading down a number of baffle plates under vacuum and then flows over coils in the heat-exchanger through which passes the deodorized fat. It enters then the heater where it is warmed up to deodorization temperatures of 225–235°C by means of condensing Dowtherm vapour (see p. 151) and finally reaches the column, where the inlet is a few feet from the top, and flows on to the top tray where the pressure is about 6 mm. Above the top tray is the vapour head space and a baffle plate arrangement at the outlet to the booster ejector to trap entrained droplets of fat. The fat passes from plate to plate in counter-current to the stripping steam until under gradually decreasing vacuum it

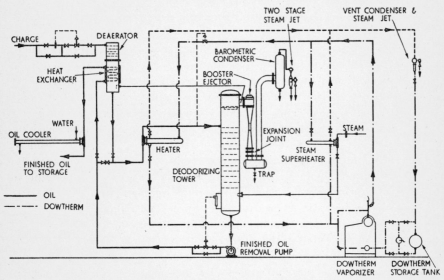

Fig. 70. Diagram of continuous deodorizing plant (Courtesy: *Foster-Wheeler Corporation, London*).

reaches the bottom, where the pressure as the result of the layers of fat on the plates and the resistance in the vapour passages has increased to about 18–25 mm abs. The amount of fat in the plant is controlled by the level of the overflow dams. Usually the passage through takes 10–15 mins., which is considered sufficient at the high temperature used. A pump, specially pressure-sealed against air leakage, removes the finished fat and pumps it through the heat-exchanger for incoming fat.

The direct steam, which can, if desired, be superheated in a separate superheater by Dowtherm, enters the column through a distributing device below the bottom plate, where it meets the deodorized fat and blows upwards through a series of nozzles on the plates. Each nozzle is covered with a cap with slotted lower edges which distribute the steam sideways into the layers of fat, so that thorough mixing and contact is established by the expanding steam. As the dams on consecutive plates are at opposite sides there is a horizontal flow of fat across the rising steam. The effect of passing the steam through a number of successive shallow layers of gradually higher concentrations of volatiles and with a large surface for the escape of vapour bubbles is stated to be a high vaporization efficiency and therefore very economic use of direct steam, and this again leads to low steam and cooling water demand in the vacuum and condensation systems. Process losses are claimed to be small, partly because the shallow layer on the top plate reduces the risk of droplets being thrown up into the vapour stream, partly because the low pressure in the layers of fat minimizes the possibility of hydrolysis.

A continuous deodorizer of this type with a tower diameter of 6 ft. has a capacity of about 5,000 lb. per hour, but plants of smaller capacities are also in use. In some installations the de-aerator is built into the column as an extension at the top.

With some apparent advantages the column deodorizer has the drawback of a decreasing vacuum from top to bottom and a slightly falling temperature. In theory the highest vacuum and temperature are needed where the concentrations of volatile substances are lowest, i.e., near the bottom. In practice there is therefore a tendency to employ temperatures up to 230–250°C to ensure a completely bland product. The principle already mentioned in connection with the early column deodorizer by *Olier* (p. 154) of using a better vacuum in the final section of the column has been applied in a recently patented column deodorizer by LEE and KING[112]. This plant is of the plate and bubble cap column type and has two zones for deodorization, a primary upper zone, where part of the volatile compounds are removed in vacuum by steam stripping, and a secondary lower zone to which the partly deodorized material is transferred from the upper zone through an external heater; fresh stripping steam at a higher vacuum is used here. The patent discloses several modifications in the ratio of returns of re-heated material to the primary and secondary zones. The finished fat is continuously removed from the secondary zone through a tubular cooler.

To avoid the drawbacks of temperature and vacuum gradients of the column deodorizers continuous plants have been designed, where the process is carried out in gradual steps in a number of successive vessels. Thus BRÜCKE in Germany[113] describes a continuous plant in which the oil flows through a number of successive vertical cylindrical vessels, for instance, seven, while being treated at decreasing temperatures from 210°C to 150°C, a common uniform vacuum being maintained on all vessels. The deodorizing temperature in the final vessel is kept relatively low so that no decomposition products are formed. The amount of oil present in each of the vessels is several times that of the rate of through-flow, and fresh stripping steam is supplied to each vessel to give vigorous circulation of the contents. It will be seen that most of the pyrolytic changes and removal of volatiles takes place in the earlier vessels at the higher temperatures, and that the last vessels serve to remove remnants of odoriferous substances. The vaporization efficiency is probably low towards the end; the steam is, of course, not used in counter-current. The use of a common vacuum system for the vessels operating at different temperatures would appear to entail some risk.

A further example of treatment in successive vessels is found in the Bataille continuous deodorizing system[114, 115], which consists of six horizontal cylindrical vessels through which the oil flows in series, each operating under a higher vacuum than the previous one (160 mm to 1 mm) and each having its separate vacuum system. In the first vessel the temperature is low enough to cause the direct steam to condense. This condensate in finely dispersed form vaporizes violently in the second and third vessels, where the temperature is increased and fresh stripping steam supplied. Still higher temperature and vacuum are applied in the fourth vessel. In the fifth the vacuum is again increased, but no direct steam is injected. The sixth vessel is for cooling the oil. In this design there are many features indicating a sound theoretical basis for deodorization, but the plant appears complicated and expensive for any advantage it might claim as regards yield and heat requirements.

Insufficient experience and information is at present available to pass a final opinion on these various multi-vessel plants.

Semi-continuous Deodorizers

The description "semi-continuous" is applied to a deodorizing plant designed by BAILEY and *The Girdler Corporation*[116], in which the fat is held for deodorization for a longer period—1–$1\frac{1}{2}$ hours—than provided in the continuous column deodorizer, and is exposed to a uniform vacuum throughout the whole height of the deodorizer; the change-over from one quality of fat to another is easily accomplished.

This deodorizer is a tall cylindrical carbon steel vessel inside which are five square superimposed nickel or stainless steel trays, provided with nickel or stainless steel heating and steaming coils. The whole vessel operates under the usual high vacuum system at about 6 mm abs. pressure. Each tray contains a 2-ft. layer of fat and has a 1-ft. headspace with louvred baffle plates above. The trays are dimensioned laterally to hold half the hourly capacity of the plant, and are fitted at the bottom with a quick-opening valve which can rapidly drain the contents of a tray into that below. As the trays are square a segmental space is left between their walls and the cylindrical shell.

Fig. 71 is a diagram of the plant, which operates as follows: A measuring tank discharges every half hour a filling to a depth of 2 ft. into the top tray, where the fat is de-aerated and heated to about 160°C by means of steam in a closed coil, while a little direct steam from a perforated coil is used for stirring and as an aid to de-aeration. After half-an-hour the contents are dropped into the second tray, where during the next half hour they are heated by Dowtherm in the closed coil to about 230°C, a little direct steam again being used for stirring. The hot fat is now dropped into the third tray, where it remains the third half hour, while most of the deodorization takes

159

place as the result of vigorous injection of direct steam. As no indirect heating coils are used the temperature falls a few degrees. The fat now passes to the fourth tray, where the same operation is repeated during the fourth half hour and deodorization finished. The deodorized fat is finally dropped into the fifth tray, where during the next half hour it is cooled by cold water in a closed coil, while just enough direct steam passes through to provide agitation to promote heat transfer. The bottom tray discharges the finished cooled fat to a drop-tank outside the deodorizer.

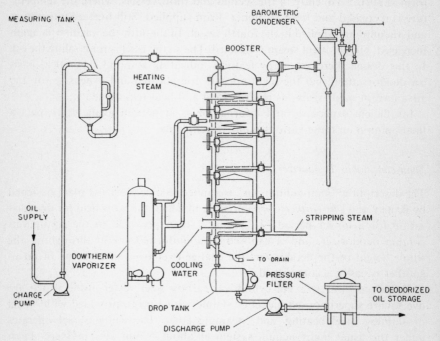

Fig. 71. Diagram of Girdler and semi-continuous deodorizing plant
(Courtesy: *Girdler Corporation, U.S.A.*).

The stripping steam and the vapours of the volatile compounds pass the baffles above the trays, where entrained fat is largely trapped, and by a hood above the baffles are deflected to the side and rise through the segmental areas at the cylinder wall to the top of the vessel where there is a connection to the vacuum system. As the vapours pass up along the wall they provide some insulation against heat losses from the trays to the shell, and any condensate formed will drain down along the wall and collect at the bottom of the vessel without risk of coming into contact with the fat. Similarly the risk of air coming into contact with the hot fat is eliminated by this arrangement, as any air leaking in would be drawn along the shell wall to the vapour outlet.

Fig. 72 shows details of a tray with closed coil for heating and the perforated coil for direct steam.

All valves are arranged for automatic opening and closing, and as the trays are completely drained before being refilled the change from one type of fat to another is comparatively simple.

By this construction of the deodorizer it is possible to maintain practically the same vacuum on all the fat subjected to stripping steam; nowhere is the hydrostatic pressure on the direct steam more than 2 ft. oil. There is a large relative surface from which the vapour bubbles escape, and with fine dispersion of the stripping steam the vaporization efficiency should be high. The fat is at least one hour at deodorization temperature and a high temperature can be used without risk of "metal effect" as the fat only comes in contact with nickel or other special inert metals. The special arrangement of the plant permits the minimum use of these expensive metals, as the trays

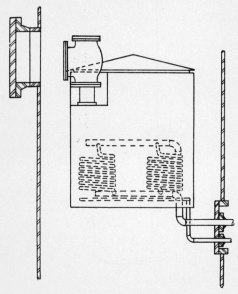

Fig. 72. Sketch of tray details, semi-continuous deodorizer.

can be constructed rather lightly, because the main strain is carried by the steel vessel.

Practical results have indicated that when operating at 6 mm abs. pressure the direct stripping steam consumption is about 4·5–5 per cent of the weight of the fat with a steam consumption for vacuum booster and steam ejectors of 17–18 per cent.

These deodorizers are 24–30 ft. high and vary in hourly capacity from 2,000–7,500 lb.

Condensation and Vacuum Plant

Before the introduction of the modern high-vacuum technique the vacuum in the deodorizer depended on the temperature of the cooling water used for condensing the vapours and on the efficiency of the vacuum pumps for removing non-condensable gases from the condenser. This method is still in use in many refineries. The vacuum pumps are either of the usual type of air compressors, reciprocating piston pumps or rotary pumps, or more frequently now in modern installations of the 2- or 3-stage steam ejector type. Condensers are either surface condensers or barometric jet condensers.

In surface condensers, an example of which is shown in Fig. 73, the vapours do not come in contact with the cooling water, and are, after condensation,

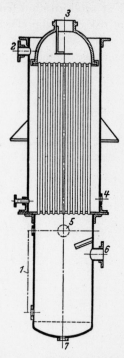

Fig. 73. Surface condenser.

1. Level indicator for condensate.
2. Overflow for cooling water.
3. Vapour inlet.
4. Inlet for cooling water.
5. Vent for air.
6. Connection to vacuum plant.
7. Drain for condensate.

collected in a vessel attached to the condenser and forming part of it. In this way a check can be kept on the amount of steam used for stripping. The non-condensed gases are removed from the condenser by the air pump. The collecting vessel for the condensate should be of sufficient size to hold all the condensate from one charge or, if used with continuous deodorizers an extraction pump must be provided for removing the condensate. Surface condensers are more expensive than jet condensers; they are mostly used where the water supply is limited and has to be re-used after intermediate cooling. As the vapours always contain some fatty matter which may be deposited on the surface of the cooling tubes the cooling effect is gradually lessened, and the condenser requires therefore careful supervision and from time to time must be dismantled and cleaned. The performance depends further on the temperature and rate of through-flow of the cooling water.

Most refiners use jet condensers, in which vapour is condensed by direct contact and mixing with the cooling water. As a rule these are arranged as barometric or high-level condensers with a fall-pipe, or tail-pipe, from the bottom of the condenser with a fall of not less than 10 metres (33 ft.) to permit the water and condensate to flow by gravity against the barometric pressure into a seal and overflow tank at the bottom of the pipe, which can also be designed to act as a separator for fatty matter in the condensate.

There are many different arrangements for contact in the jet condensers, but in principle they are mostly arranged for counter-current flow of water and vapour, the former entering at the higher level of the condenser through a spraying or distributing device, the latter at the lower level. Fig. 74 shows

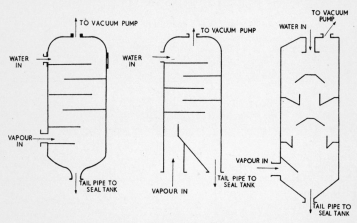

Fig. 74. Types of jet condensers.

some types of counter-current arrangements with plates for cascading the water down against the rising vapour. At the highest point is the connection to the air pump or steam jets for withdrawing the non-condensable vapours and any air which might have been contained in the cooling water. At the bottom is the tail-pipe for the barometric leg, through which water and condensate is removed to the seal tank.

Fig. 75 shows a condenser where the vapours enter through the central pipe 2 and follow the path shown by the arrow in counter-current to the water, which enters at 3 and runs on to tray (a_1), overflows to trays (c_1), (a_2), (c_2) and (a_3), mixes with and condenses the vapours and leaves with the condensate through the tail pipe at the bottom, while non-condensable gases are drawn off by pump or jets at 1.

If through limitation on the amount of cooling water available it is necessary to re-use some of it, it should be cooled after separation and trapping of fatty matter. This cooling can for example be done as illustrated in Fig.

163

76 by evaporating some of the circulating water in an atmospheric cooling-tower.

If the shortage is so great that it all has to be re-used it may be an advantage to use surface condensers, or to adopt a system of compound condensation,

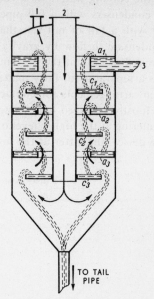

Fig. 75.   Jet condenser.

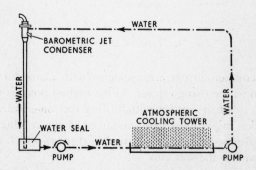

Fig. 76.   Scheme for cooling condenser water.

in which two condensers are used, one above the other. The cooling-water-condensate mixture is discharged from the upper to the lower condenser through a water seal. A part of the vapours is condensed in the upper condenser; the remainder is drawn by a steam jet ejector and injected into the lower condenser, where it is condensed together with the jet steam at the higher pressure ruling there.

The barometric counter-current jet condenser is the simplest in construction, supervision and maintenance, and because of the direct contact of vapours and cooling water it makes the most economic use of the supplies available. If there is insufficient height to provide the "barometric" fall through the tail-pipe the water and condensate must be removed by an extraction pump.

Provided the dry air pump or the steam jet ejector can cope efficiently with the non-condensable gases, the vacuum which can be attained depends on the discharge temperature of the cooling water. The maximum vacuum obtainable is that which corresponds to the tension of saturated water vapour at the temperature of the discharge from the condenser plus the partial pressures of the vapours and non-condensable gas that enters the condenser;

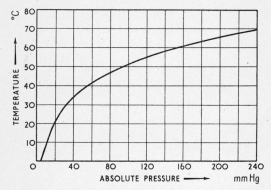

Fig. 77. Relation between temperature and pressure of saturated water vapour.

the latter are, however, under the conditions ruling very small and negligible, provided there are no air leakages.

Fig. 77 shows the relation between the temperature of water and the tension of saturated water vapour. Where cold water is available, for instance, from deep wells or under winter conditions in temperate climates, a deodorizer vacuum corresponding to 15–20 mm abs. pressure may be obtained, but in warm climates it may be difficult to get pressures below 50–60 mm unless vacuum augmentors are used.

The ratios of cooling water to vapour which are required in a barometric jet condenser to obtain various absolute pressures in the vacuum system are shown graphically in Fig. 78 where the ordinates give the inlet temperatures of the cooling water, the abscissae the pressures obtainable with the water: vapour ratios shown by the curves.

Fig. 79 is a diagrammatic illustration of the customary arrangement of a deodorizer with oil trap and barometric jet condenser.

The dependence of the vacuum on the temperature of the cooling water is avoided by the use of vacuum augmentors or boosters on the principle of steam jet compressors. Although the modern high-vacuum technique makes

165

it possible to reduce the abs. pressure to a small fraction of a millimetre, economic and practical considerations generally limit the vacuum used in deodorization to that corresponding to an abs. pressure of 3–4 mm; more common pressures are 6–10 mm.

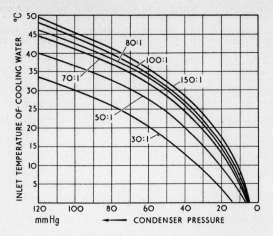

Fig. 78.   Ratio of cooling water to vapour.

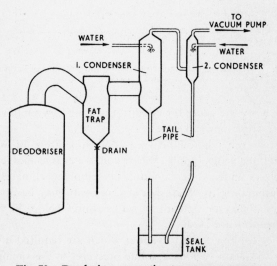

Fig. 79.   Deodorizer connection to vacuum system.

Fig. 80 shows the principle of using a vacuum augmentor. Without this device the vacuum would, as in the plant in Fig. 79, depend on the air pump and condenser water. By operating the steam jet vacuum augmentor the high velocity of the jet steam imparts some of the momentum to the vapours, which are drawn into the jet, thereby increasing the vacuum in the deodorizer, and compresses the vapours to the higher pressure corresponding to the condensation conditions, i.e., quantity and temperature of the cooling water. In this way it is possible to operate the deodorizer at a better vacuum than otherwise governed by the cooling water. In Fig. 80, D is the deodorizer, V the vapour pipe, F a fat-trap, A the vacuum augmentor or booster, C_1 the primary condenser, C_2 the secondary condenser, E_1 and E_2 steam jet ejectors for maintaining vacuum conditions in the condensers by removing non-condensed gases; E_3 is a steam jet ejector for drawing a vacuum on the plant when starting up.

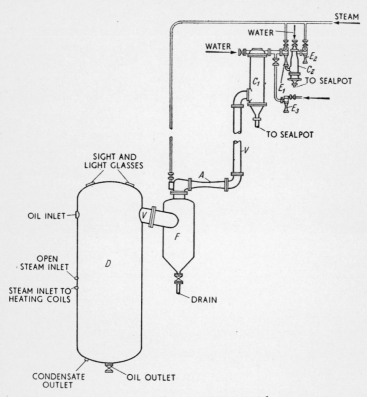

Fig. 80.   Deodorizer connections to augmentor and vacuum system.

This method of augmenting the vacuum was first applied to deodorization by the *Lurgi Gesellschaft für Warmetechnik* in Germany[117], not only for the purpose of inserting an augmentor between deodorizer and condenser, but also to arrange progressive deodorization in two vessels in series, for which process a high economic utilization of the steam is claimed. The part-deodorized oil in the post-deodorizer is completely deodorized with fresh direct steam under high vacuum (6–8 mm abs. pressure) produced by a steam jet vacuum augmentor, and the steam from the post-deodorizer plus the augmentor steam provides the direct steam for the pre-deodorization which is done under the vacuum provided by the barometric condenser system.

Fig. 81 shows a diagram of this plant. *a* is the secondary or post-deodorizer *c* is the inlet for the part-deodorized oil. C_1 the outlet for the finished oil. *b* is the primary or pre-deodorizer with inlet *d* for untreated oil and outlet D_1 for part-deodorized oil. *b* is via fat-trap *f* connected to the barometric condenser *h* by the vapour pipe *e*. *i* is the connection from the condenser to the vacuum air pump for non-condensable gases. *a* is via fat trap f_1 connected to the steam jet vacuum augmentor *n*, which gets its dry operating steam from the boiler steam supply at *S* and discharges it together with the vapour from *a* via the pipe *o* into the deodorizer *b* through a perforated distribution pipe. S_1 is the supply of fresh direct steam to deodorizer *a*. Both deodorizers are further equipped with coils for indirect heating and cooling.

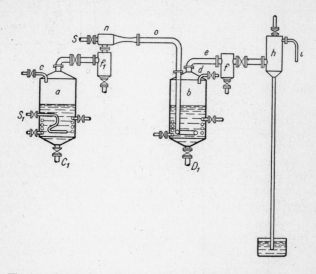

Fig. 81. Deodorizer plant, according to *Metallgesellschaft A. G.*

When the deodorizers have been charged with oil the valve to the condenser is opened and the plant put under vacuum. The augmentor is then started up and delivers its steam to the distributor in *b*. Simultaneously the valve in the direct steam supply to the distributor in *a* is opened and steam injected. This and volatile compounds from *a* are then together with the operating steam from the augmentor passed to the distributor in *b*. In a later patent it is recommended to interpose a fat-separator in the pipe line *o* to trap entrained traces of fatty matter, which through the frequently strong cooling that takes place by the energy transfer in the diffuser of the jet, may condense there.

In the early days of high-vacuum deodorization this type of plant was installed in several refineries, but has now probably been superseded by more modern plant for continuous or batchwise high-vacuum operation. These are usually fitted with an augmentor for maintaining an operating pressure on the surface of the fat of 4–6 mm abs. The jets are designed to work with dry steam of a minimum pressure, but high pressure steam is not essential; jets are designed for pressures as low as 2 atm. The amount of jet steam needed for the augmentor is larger than that used as direct steam in the deodorizer, 2–4 times, but the combined amount is less than would be required for deodorizing if this process had to be operated at the higher pressure necessary in the absence of the augmentor. Fig. 82 shows a graph from tests relating steam consumption without augmentor to the total steam consumption with augmentor in kilos per hour per ton fat in

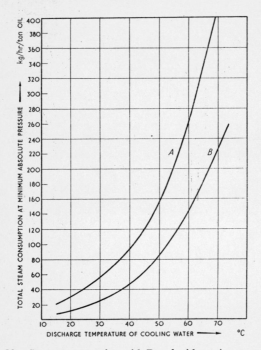

Fig. 82.   Steam consumption with B and without A augmentor.

the deodorizer, when working at condenser pressures corresponding to the discharge temperature of the cooling water. The graph shows that the total steam consumption is always less with than without augmentor.

The augmentor steam with the steam and vapours from the deodorizer is discharged into a barometric jet condenser, where it is condensed by the cooling water while non-condensable gases are removed by a steam jet ejector, usually of the 2- or 3-stage type. Fig. 83 shows a 2-stage ejector[118]. J connects to the deodorizer, A is the condenser with cooling water sprays E, O the outlet for the water and condensate to a barometric fall-pipe. Non-condensable gases are withdrawn through B by steam ejector C and discharged into an intermediate or secondary condenser D meeting a spray of water from E_1. The condensate from this condenser is withdrawn at O_1

through a barometric fall-pipe and the uncondensed gases are carried by the secondary jet ejector F to the atmosphere.

Fig. 84 illustrates an equipment for a batch deodorizer of 10 tons working capacity, designed to operate at 5 mm abs. pressure. It consists of the augmentor A with connection I to the deodorizer, main condenser C with outlet O to the barometric fall-pipe, steam jet ejectors D and E and secondary condenser C_1 for the steam from D. There is also a powerful ejector F for

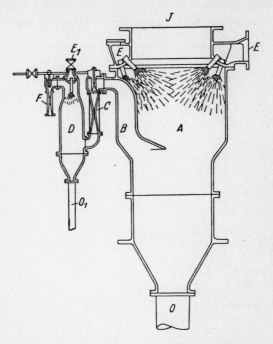

Fig. 83.   Jet condenser with 2-stage steam jet ejector.

rapidly creating the vacuum when starting up the plant. For such equipment the following performance figures are given:

Open steam from deodorizer . . .	300 lb. per hour.
Steam pressure for jets	150 lb. sq. i.g.
Steam for augmentor and ejectors . .	730 lb. per hour.
Maximum cooling water temperature . .	70°F.
Cooling water required	7,000 gal. per hour.

As the time to obtain a suitable quality would be about 3 hours the total steam consumption would be 3,090 lb. or 13·5 per cent of the weight of the contents. Of this steam less than one-third is direct steam for the deodorizer. The cooling water ratio to total steam is about 70:1.

Fig. 85 is a diagram of the layout of a barometric jet condensing plant with or without augmentor[119]. The cooling water for the principal and for

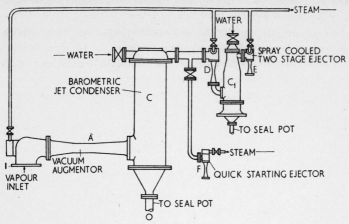

Fig. 84. General arrangement of Hick Hargreaves vacuum equipment with augmentor for deodorizing.

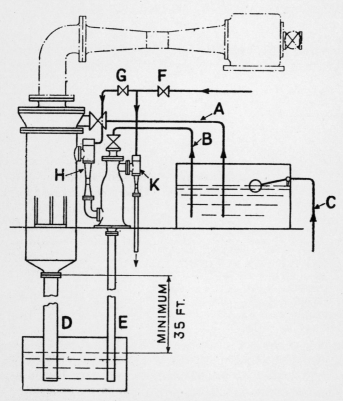

Fig. 85. Diagram of steam and water connections to barometric jet condensing plant.

171

the secondary condenser is drawn through separate pipes *A* and *B* from the water supply tank where the level is kept constant by a ball float valve controlling the supply through *C*. Separate barometric fall-pipes *D* and *E* are provided for the two condensers. Valves *F* and *G* for the ejector jets *H* and *K* are arranged so that steam cannot be admitted to the primary ejector unless first flowing to the secondary one.

Each deodorizer should have its separate condensation and vacuum plant. Some refineries have vapour off-takes from several deodorizers joining into a common duct to the vacuum plant. This is to be deprecated, as starting and stopping of deodorizers may cause irregularity of working in other units.

Fat-Traps

The temperature of the shell at the top of the deodorizer and of the vapour ducts is always lower than that of the surface of the fat from which the vapours rise. Some condensation of odoriferous compounds, fatty acids, etc.,

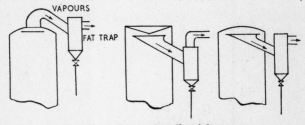

Fig. 86. Vapour take-off and fat traps.

may therefore occur there. It is important that this should not fall back into the fat, and various arrangements of the vapour off-take have been designed for that purpose. Fig. 86 shows some constructions from batch deodorizers. It is inadvisable to have a long vertical vapour off-take from the deodorizer, as in spite of the high vapour speed, caused by the constriction of the passage, it is difficult to prevent some back-flow of condensate.

A fat-trap is frequently fitted in the vapour pipe between the deodorizer and the vacuum augmentor or condenser to collect this condensate. Fig. 87 shows an example of a cylindrical trap which at *B* connects with the deodorizer, at *C* with the vapour pipe, and at *A* has an outlet from which the condensate that collects at the bottom can be drained periodically.

Superheaters for Steam

While in the earlier days of refining it was the general practice to use superheated steam as direct steam for deodorizing, ordinary dry boiler steam is now mostly used. Special precautions are, however, frequently taken to ensure that the feed water for the boilers is clean and de-aerated to avoid oxygen and odorous matters in the steam. Saturated steam, after passing the inlet valve and orifice plate to the deodorizer, comes under the influence of the vacuum and the high fat temperature and becomes superheated at once at the prevailing pressure. The possibility of a trace of moisture being present and giving rise to slight hydrolysis is small, and if there should be a trace it might have a beneficial effect on the pyrolysis of some odoriferous compounds.

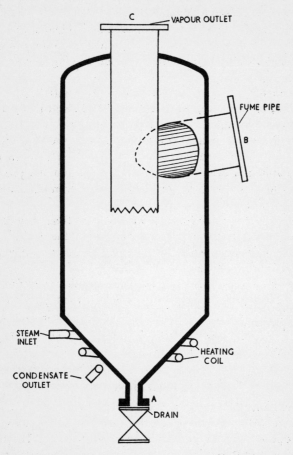

Fig. 87. Fat-trap (Courtesy: *W. J. Fraser & Co. Ltd., Dagenham*).

In refineries where specially superheated steam is preferred, usually of 250–300°C, separate superheaters are an advantage to avoid fluctuations in temperature due to uneven demand on the boilers, as well as from the deodorizers. Such superheaters must therefore be easy to regulate, and should respond quickly to varying demands. For that reason oil-firing is mostly preferred.

Superheaters in which the heating medium is Dowtherm vapour are used with some deodorizers, both for batch and continuous operation (see Fig. 66, p. 152).

Oil Coolers

After deodorization the contents should be cooled as quickly as possible to 60°C or lower before being exposed to air. This is often done in the deodorizer by using the closed steam coils for circulation of cooling water, while maintaining the vacuum and using a small amount of direct steam for stirring and to allow a slight steam flow through the vacuum system, until the temperature is reduced to about 80°C.

Some refiners prefer to cool the deodorized oil in separate vacuum coolers, cylindrical vessels with cooling coils dimensioned for rapid cooling of the oil, and provided with stirrers to ensure regular cooling and improved heat transfer.

A mixture of the two systems is often used. The initial cooling is done in the deodorizer, for instance, down to 100–125°C, and the final cooling in the separate vacuum cooler.

When the deodorizer is used for cooling a little more steam is required to bring the vessel and the next charge up to deodorization temperature than when cooling is done in a separate vessel, and the process cycle is prolonged by an hour or more; on the other hand an extra vacuum vessel with auxiliaries is saved.

Continuous coolers in the form of water-cooled tubular coolers are used for continuous deodorizers and generally constitute the final cooling section in a heat-exchange system, where the outgoing deodorized oil is first used for pre-heating the incoming charge.

Fig. 88 shows a vertical section of a vacuum oil cooler for a charge of 10 tons. The deodorized oil enters the vessel near the top, and when hot fills it to about 75 per cent of its volume. During cooling it contracts to about the level of the helical triple coil of cooling tubes. The cooler is provided with an agitator with paddle blades.

THE DEODORIZATION PROCESS

In batch operations the procedure is as follows:

The vacuum plant is started up, the valve in the vacuum duct at the deodorizer opened and the vessel placed under vacuum. The bleached fat, generally at a temperature of 60°C or more, is drawn in by vacuum, if possible, and if the inlet pipe is near to the top of the deodorizer a partial de-aeration of the fat takes place during filling. When the full charge is drawn in, the fat should cover the heating coils, and heating to deodorization temperature should be as rapid as possible. Heat transfer is improved by admitting a moderate stream of direct steam through the distributor as soon as the temperature is high enough to prevent condensation of steam at the low pressure ruling in the vessel, usually when the temperature is 70–80°C. As the temperature increases more direct steam is injected, and when deodorization temperature approaches, the steam flow should be sufficient to cause a brisk and lively ebullition without violent release of vapour. The direct steam is generally supplied at about 2 atm. pressure at the orifice valve, but the pressure falls rapidly, and at the point of injection in the deodorizers is largely determined by the height of the column of fat. The temperature of deodorization is controlled by the heating coils, and this as well as the period of deodorization varies widely with the vacuum available and the kind and quality of fat under treatment, which is continued until a sample, drawn

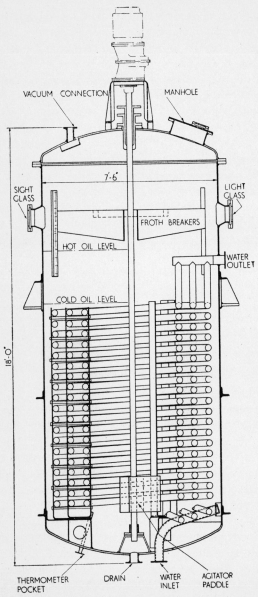

VACUUM CONNECTION   MANHOLE

SIGHT GLASS

7·6'

LIGHT GLASS

FROTH BREAKERS

HOT OIL LEVEL

WATER OUTLET

COLD OIL LEVEL

18-0"

THERMOMETER POCKET   DRAIN   WATER INLET   AGITATOR PADDLE

Fig. 88.   Oil cooler, 10 ton capacity (Courtesy: *Bamag, Ltd., London*).

and cooled under vacuum, is satisfactory. In most cases complete blandness of flavour is the aim, but with certain oils, intended for use as salad oils or for other edible oil purposes, some of the characteristic flavour is often retained.

When ordinary steel vessels are used the temperature should not exceed 185–190°C, except for very short periods, as otherwise a "metal" flavour and darkening of colour may develop. Where higher temperatures are employed special inert metals should be used.

Of highest importance is the vacuum. The better the vacuum the higher is the "safe" temperature that can be used, and the shorter the time required for completion of the operation. The volatility of the odoriferous components and the volume of the amount of direct steam, on which the velocity of the process depends, increase with the vacuum; hence the higher the vacuum the larger the output from the plant and the smaller the consumption of steam.

Many refiners specify a minimum period of deodorization, 3–8 hours, according to the kind of fat, hydrogenated fat as a rule needing shorter treatment than natural fats. The hourly flow of steam is then adjusted to give at the vacuum available the amount of steam considered adequate for the particular fat.

Most of the volatile components are evaporated rather rapidly and the bulk of the steam is needed for removing the last traces, which unless they are eliminated may affect unfavourably the flavour stability of the deodorized fat, particularly if used in margarine, for which a bland product of high stability is required.

When deodorization is finished the fat is cooled as rapidly as possible. As described earlier under "Oil Coolers" (p. 174) this can be done in the deodorizer or in a separate cooler or in both. It is done under vacuum, and while the fat is in the deodorizer a reduced flow of direct steam is injected into the fat, partly for agitation during cooling, partly because continuation of steam flow is essential, as long as the vessel is connected to the vacuum system, to present a back-flow of vapours as the deodorizer cools down.

Where deodorizers are connected with auxiliary external vacuum coolers for final cooling, steam injection in the deodorizer usually ceases at 90–100°C and the connection to the vacuum system is closed. It is, however, advisable to maintain, by means of a small steam jet, a flow of steam in the vapour pipe between the deodorizer valve and the condenser as a precaution against leakage back into the deodorizer. In the meantime the external cooler has been connected to the high vacuum system, and the pre-cooled fat from the deodorizer is run in to be cooled further down under vacuum by cooling coils with water, and sometimes also a cooling jacket, while circulation is maintained by stirrer. When the fat has been cooled to the appropriate temperature the connection from the cooler to the vacuum system is closed and the vacuum in the cooler broken, sometimes with an inert gas. The fat is now ready for use, although some refiners prefer to give it a final filtration.

176

When there are no external coolers the fat is usually cooled to 70–75°C or lower in the deodorizer before the connection to the vacuum system is closed. The vacuum in the vessel is broken by means of inert gas and the contents further cooled to the desired temperature.

With deodorizers where other heating media than steam are used, for instance, coils for circulating mineral oil or Dowtherm vapour, all the cooling is done in separate vacuum coolers or by pumping the fat through tubular coolers. This method is also frequently adopted with steam-heated deodorizers to avoid cooling the vessel down.

The operations of the continuous and semi-continuous deodorizers are explained under the description of the plants.

Crude oils and fats in their natural state contain very small proportions of compounds which act as antioxidants, for instance, phosphatide fractions, tocopherols, phenolic compounds and some not yet identified. A considerable proportion of these is eliminated, destroyed or inactivated in the refinery operations. Refined deodorized oils consequently often show less resistance to oxidation than crude oils, particularly those with the more unsaturated fatty acid radicals. Many refiners therefore add some ingredients to the oil in the deodorizer to increase its resistance to oxidation during the high temperature treatment and during subsequent storage. Such additions act partly to immobilize certain oxidation catalysts, such as minute traces of iron and other metals, partly as synergists with antioxidants which have passed through previous processes, for instance, tocopherols. The most common additions are acid compounds, lactic, phosphoric, tartaric or citric acids. The proportion is very small, 0·005–0·01 per cent citric acid[120, 121, 122]. It is advantageous to add it as a strong aqueous solution at the beginning of the deodorization, but as it is largely eliminated during the process it is desirable to add a proportion of it when cooling begins.

REFERENCES

[1] SCHAFRANOWSKAJA, W. I.; Metody Analisa w maslobojno-shirowoj Promyschlennosti 1936, 89.
[2] B.P. 326,539.
[3] B.P. 366,996.
[4] BAUMAN, M. and I. GRABOWSKI; Masloboino Shirowoje Djelo 1936 **12** 237.
[5] B.P. 377,336.
[6] B.P. 393,108.
[7] Can. P. 330,967.
[8] D.R.P. 565,079.
[9] U.S.P. 1,937,320.
[10] D.R.P. 569,797 and 592,089.
[11] THURMAN, B. H.; J. Ind. Eng. Chem. 1923 **15** 395.
[12] U.S.P. 1,737,402.
[13] U.S.P. 1,747,675.
[14] U.S.P. 1,448,581.
[15] U.S.P. 1,725,895.
[16] NJEMIROWSKI, O; Chem. Zentrbl. 1929 **2** 3077. Abstract from Masloboino Shirowoje Djelo 1929 No. 2 12–14.
[17] Fr. Pat. 723,634.
[18] SINOWJEW, A.; Arb. Zentr. Rus. Fat Forsch. U.S.S.R. 1934 **3** 3.
[19] B.P. 371,503.

[20] B.P. 341,390.
[21] LEIMDORFER, J; Seifensieder Z. 1933 **60** 84.
[22] B.P. 362,964.
[23] THURMAN, B. H.; J. Ind. Eng. Chem. 1923 **15** 395.
[24] WESSON, D.; J. Oil and Fat Ind. 1926 **3**, 297.
JAMIESON, G. S.; Vegetable Fats and Oils. Reinhold Publ. Co., New York 1943.
[25] American Oil Chemists' Society Official and Tentative Methods, 1946.
[26] DRESSLER, R. G.; Oil and Soap 1940 **17** 6.
[27] B.P. 407,995; U.S.P. 2,050,844.
[28] B.P. 390,805; U.S.P. 2,100,276.
[29] JAMES, E. M.; Oil and Soap 1934 **11** 137.
[30] U.S.P. 2,341,536–2,342,042–2,512,245.
[31] SCHMIDT, A. and O. MICHAILOWSKAJA; Masloboino Shirowoje Djelo 1935 **11** 255.
[32] AYERS, E.; Chem. Metallurg. Eng. 1920 **23** 1025.
[33] THURMAN, B. H.; J. Ind. Eng. Chem. 1932 **24** 1187.
[34] DRESSLER, R. G.; Oil and Soap 1940 **17** 124.
[35] CLAYTON, B. and *Refining Inc.*; U.S.P. 2,190,593/4/5; U.S.P. 2,249,701/2.
[36] MATTIKOW, M.; J. Amer. Oil Chem. Soc. 1948 **25** 200.
[37] HEFTER, G.; Technologie der Oels und Fette I, 654. Berlin 1905.
[38] WECKER, E.; D.R.P. 397,332. U.S.P. 1,622,126, B.P. 213,267–277,085.
[39] WILLIAMS, A. E.; Chem. Age 1948 **61** 245.
[40] CRAIG, R. and *Lever Brothers Ltd.*; B.P. 224,928 and 242,316.
[41] CLAYTON, B.; U.S.P. 2,478,089.
[42] TAYLOR, T. I., LARSON, L. and W. JOHNSON; J. Ind. Eng. Chem. 1936 **28** 616.
[43] BOLLMANN, H.; U.S.P. 2,478,089.
[44] SCHLENKER, E.; D.R.P. 551,356.
[45] *Pittsburgh Plate Glass Co.*, U.S.P. 2,200,390/1.
[46] GLOYER, S. W.; J. Ind. Eng. Chem. 1948 **40** 228.
[47] ——; J. Amer. Oil Chem. Soc. 1949 **26** 162.
[48] *M. W. Kellog Co.* U.S.P. 2,454,638 and 2,467,906.
[49] HIXON, A. W., and J. B. BOCKELMAN; Trans. Amer. Inst. Chem. Eng. 1942 **38** 891.
[50] FEUGE, R. O., BAILEY, A. E. and E. A. KRAMER; Oil and Soap 1945 **22** 202.
[51] SCHLINCK, J.; B.P. 334,659 and D.R.P. 315,222.
[52] SWIFT, *et al.*; Oil and Soap 1944 **21** 317.
[53] THURMAN, B. H.; J. Ind. Eng. Chem. 1932. **24** 1187.
[54] FREUNDLICH, H.; Capillarchemie, 4th ed. 1930 **1** 244; Colloid and Capillary Chemistry, p. 172, London 1926.
[55] BAILEY, A. E.; Industrial Oil and Fat Products, p. 529, New York 1945.
[56] HASSLER, J. W. and R. A. HAGBERG,; Oil and Soap 1939 **16** 188.
[57] BENEDICT, C. W.; J. Oil and Fat Ind. 1925 **2** 62.
[58] DECKERT, R; Seifens. Ztg. 1925 **52** 754.
[59] DAVIS, C. W. and L. R. MESSER; U.S.A. Tech. Publication No. 207, 1929.
[60] LJALIN, L. M. and N. A. WARISINA; J. Chem. Ind. (Russia) 1927 **4** 882.
[61] UENO, S.; J. Ind. Eng. Chem. 1915 **7** 596.
[62] KERR, P. F.; Amer. Mineralogist 1932 **17** 192.
[63] HOFMANN, U., ENDELL, K. and D. WILM; Angew. Chem. 1934 **47** 539.
[64] SCHOENFELD, H.; Neuere Verf. zur Raff. Fette und Oele, p. 67. Berlin 1931.
[65] VAGELER, P. and K. ENDELL; D.R.P. 597,716.
[66] FOGLE, M. E. and H. L. OLIN; J. Ind. Eng. Chem. 1933 **25** 1070.
[67] HOFMANN, U. and K. ENDELL; Angew. Chem. 1935 **48** 187.
[68] ECKART, O.; *ibid* 1929 **42** 939.
[69] SCHULTZE, G. R.; *ibid.* 1936 **49** 74.
[70] HOFMANN, U. *et al.*; Z. Kristall. Krist.-phys. and -chemie. 1933 **86** 346.
[71] VOIGT, A.; Fettchem. Umschau 1926 **43** 49.
[72] KULKARNI, B. S. and S. K. K. JATKAR; Curr. Science 1936 **5** 18.
[73] BURGHARDT, O.; J. Ind. Eng. Chem. 1931 **23** 800.
[74] F.I.A.T. 810, F.I.A.T. TB/T40 and B.I.O.S. 398.
[75] ECKART, O. and WIRZMÜLLER; Die Bleicherden, 2 ed., p. 35, 1929.
[76] MECKLENBURG, W.; Angew. Chem. 1924 **37** 873.
[77] BAILLEUL, G., HERBERT, W. and E. REISEMANN; Aktive Kohlen, p. 13, Stuttgart 1934.
[78] OSTREYKO, R.; D.R.P. 136,792.
[79] PICK, H. and R. KRAUS; Kolloidchem. Beihefte 1932 **35** 245.
[80] KREZIL, F. Die Adsorptionstechnik, p. 13, Dresden, 1935.
[81] SCHOENFELD, H.; Allgem. Oel und Fett Z. 1929 **26** 508.
[82] SCHOENFELD, H.; Neuere Verf. Raff. Oele and Fetten, p. 81. Berlin 1931.
[83] KING, R. R. and F. W. WHARTON; J. Amer. Oil Chem. Soc. 1949 **26** 389. U.S.P. 2,428,082.
[84] HASSLER, J. W. and R. A. HAGBERG; Oil and Soap 1939 **16** 188.

[85] *The Girdler Corporation:* Private communication.
[86] D.R.P. 576,852.
[87] JAYNES, V. H. and J. O. OSBURN; J. Amer. Oil Chem. Soc. 1949 **26** *693*.
[88] GEORGI, C. D. V. and G. L. TEIK; Malayan Agr. J. 1933 **21** 23.
[89] —— and T. D. MARSH; *ibid.* 1933 **21** 505.
[90] SCHAEFER, W. and G. BITTER; Seifens Z. 1933 **60** 789.
[91] LANGENKAMP, P.; Z. Deutsch. Oel und Fettind. 1925 **45** 621.
[92] JORDAN, A.; Oele, Fette, Wachse, Seifen, Kosmetik, 1936, 3.
[93] Austrian Patent 137,324 (1932).
[94] French Patent 762,166 (1933).
[95] B.P. 577,879.
[96] *Lever Brothers and Unilever Ltd.* B.P. 598,420.
[97] *Lever Brothers and Unilever Ltd.* B.P. 557,618. B.P. 578,102.
[98] MARCELET, H.; C.R. Acad. Sci. 1936 **202** 867 and 1809; J. Pharm. Chim. (8) 1936 **24** 213.
[99] HALLER, A. and LASSIEUR, A.; Compt. rend. 1910 **150** 1013; *ibid.* 1911 **151** 697.
[100] SALWAY, A. H.; J. Chem. Soc. 1917 **111** 407.
[101] JASPERSON, H. and R. JONES; J. Soc. Chem. Ind. 1947T, 13.
[102] SCHOENFELD, H.; Chemie und Technologie der Fette und Fettprodukte, Vol. II, p. 507, T. Springer, Vienna 1937.
[103] POOL, W. O. and A. W. RALSTON; J. Ind. Eng. Chem. 1942 **34** 1104.
[104] PERRY, J. H.; Chemical Engineer's Handbook, 1950, p. 583.
[105] BRASH, W.; J. Soc. Chem. Ind. 45, 73T and 45, 331T (1926).
[106] SINGER, M.; Seifens Z. 1938 **65** 487 and 507.
[107] BAILEY, A. E.; J. Ind. Eng. Chem. 1941 **33** 404.
[108] BATES, R. W.; J. Amer. Oil Chem. Soc. 1949 **26** 601.
[109] SOUDERS, M. and G. G. BROWN; J. Ind. Eng. Chem. 1934 **26** 98.
[110] Dowtherm Tables; *Dow Chemical Co.*
[111] BOLLMANN, H.; D.R.P. 412,160.
[112] LEE, A. P. and W. G. KING; B.P. 589,534.
[113] BRÜCKE, O.; D.R.P. 723,436.
[114] BATAILLE, R.; French Patent 954,496.
[115] BATAILLE, R.; Oléagineux 1948 3 532.
[116] BAILEY, A. E.; J. Amer. Oil Chem. Soc. 1949 **26** 166.
[117] D.R.P. 496,434.
[118] ARROWSMITH, G.; Trans. Inst. Chem. Eng. 1949 **27** 106.
[119] —— *ibid.* 1949 **27** 109.
[120] GOSS, W. H.; Oil and Soap 1946 **23** 241.
[121] SCHWAB, A. W. *et al.*; J. Amer. Oil Chem. Soc. 1949 **26** 441.
[122] LEMON, H. W. *et al.*; Can. J. Res. 1950 28F 453.
[123] THURMAN, B. H.; J. Ind. Eng. Chem. 1923 **15** 395.

3

PROCESS CONTROL

FROM the commercial point of view the important data are the weights of the crude fat entering the process and of the finished fat. On these figures the cost of the process is based after due credit is taken for the value of the by-products. The technical control analyses the shrinkage in material to ascertain the avoidable and unavoidable losses in order to keep the former at a minimum.

The crude fat contains in addition to the glycerides—including small amounts of mono- and diglycerides—usually moisture, solid suspended impurities from the seeds, etc., gums, phosphatides, colouring matters, flavour compounds and free fatty acids. The ideal process would be that which yields 100 per cent of the glycerides present in the crude fat, but that is not possible in practice. Some glyceride is lost but should, like the phosphatides and free fatty acids, mostly be recovered as a by-product of lower value.

Moisture is even in well settled crude fats generally present to the extent of 0·25–0·5 per cent. It is eliminated in the refining process and its loss is intended. It can be the cause of increased loss, as storage of wet fat, particularly at the temperature necessary for keeping it in liquid form, may lead to hydrolysis by enzymic and bacterial action and thus to increase in the free fatty acid content and loss of neutral oil. This potential increase in free fatty acids is particularly liable to occur if the crude fat contains some "foots" from the crushing or extraction process.

The "foots", together with gums, mucilage, etc., which may amount to 0·1–0·2 per cent of the crude fat, also forms part of the intended loss. They are sometimes removed in a pre-treatment, sometimes in the neutralization process. In either case their elimination entails a small loss of neutral fat, equal to 50–100 per cent of the weight of the impurities. This loss of neutral fat may partly be recovered as a low-grade by-product.

The phosphatide content of crude fats varies considerably; soya bean oil may contain 2–2·5 per cent, some oils and fats as little as 0·1–0·2 per cent or even less. Some liquid oils, particularly soya bean oil, are frequently treated, when freshly extracted, for the removal and recovery of the phosphatides as a valuable by-product. From those not specially treated 60–70 per cent of the phosphatides are removed either by a de-gumming pre-treatment or in course of neutralization, and a high percentage of this intended loss is recoverable as a low-grade by-product.

Removal of the free fatty acids by neutralization or de-acidification entails an unavoidable loss of some neutral fat, partly absorbed or emulsified as such in the soap solution, partly as soap from saponification of neutral fat when excess of alkali is used for neutralization. While the removal of the free fatty acids is an intended refining loss, the refiner strives to keep the concomitant loss of neutral fat as low as possible. The "refining factor"—the ratio of neutralization loss to free fatty acids in the crude fat (see p. 39)—varies considerably with types and qualities of fats, neutralization methods, pre-treatment etc. Usually it is between 1·3 and 2. All the fatty matter in the soapstock is recoverable if the latter is used direct in soap. If, as frequently is the case, the fatty matter in the soapstock is separated by acidulation as "acid oil", a slight loss occurs. The soapstock or the "acid oil" contain in concentration most of the impurities and degradation products from the crude fat, and is therefore inferior in quality to the crude fat itself. The ratio of free fatty acids to neutral fat in the "acid oil" or of soap fatty matter to neutral fat in the soapstock depends on the neutralization conditions, excess of alkali, etc. ; the neutral fat in the total fatty matter in the soapstock or "acid oil" varies usually between 10 per cent and 50 per cent, but should in efficient refineries not exceed 25–30 per cent.

A slight loss of neutral fat arises from the washing of the neutralized fat; it should not exceed 0·1 per cent.

A serious source of loss is the adsorption bleaching. The actual weight of colouring matter and traces of soap which may be present in the fat after alkali neutralization is insignificant; by their removal a much larger weight of fat is retained in the adsorbent, and although most of the fat can be recovered from the spent adsorbent, as described in the chapter "Oil Recovery from Bleaching Residue" (p. 125), it is heavily degraded in value. The percentage lost in this way varies widely with the percentage and type of adsorbent. If, for instance, a fat requires 2 per cent adsorbent for satisfactory bleaching, as much as 1·3–1·7 per cent fat, calculated on the neutralized fat, may be retained. Although 1–1·4 per cent may be recovered as a lower-grade fat there is an irrecoverable loss of about 0·3 per cent or more.

A further loss is attributable to the bleaching process where this is done with an acid-activated earth under conditions which lead to hydrolysis of some of the neutral fat; increases in free fatty acids through this cause of 0·2–0·3 per cent are fairly common. These free fatty acids are distilled off in the subsequent deodorization and are largely recovered as a very low-grade trap fat, mixed with odoriferous volatile compounds of doubtful commercial value.

The weight of odoriferous compounds from the deodorization process is small, 0·1–0·2 per cent, but some fat entrained in the current of steam and some fatty acids from slight hydrolysis during deodorization, as well as the eventual fatty acids from bleaching just referred to, may bring the loss up to about 0·5 per cent. Most of this distillate is trapped and classified as low-grade trap fat. A small proportion is lost in the cooling water from the jet condensers. While, of course, the removal of the odoriferous and unstable compounds is an intended loss, the deodorization process should be con-ducted in such a manner that the other losses are minimized. The higher the vacuum the less steam is required, and this, together with a suitable rate of steaming, facilitates the vaporization of the volatile compounds and reduces the risk of hydrolysis and entrainment of neutral fat.

Table VIII shows a process balance analysis for a fat with 2 per cent free fatty acids in the crude material, by way of example; analyses have further shown that it contains 0·3 per cent moisture and coarse fat-insoluble impurities and 0·5 per cent phosphatides and gums. The glyceride content is therefore 97·2 per cent. The weight of the finished fat was 93·4 per cent of the weighed-in crude fat.

TABLE VIII

Source of Loss	Amount Lost (%)	Amount Recovered as By-product (%)
Moisture and Impurities	0·3	—
Phosphatides and gums	0·6	0·6
Fatty matter in soapstock	3·3	3·2
„ „ wash-water	0·2	0·1
„ „ bleaching residue	1·5	1·2
Material lost in deodorization	0·5	0·4
Total	6·4	5·5

Finished oil 93·4% + losses accounted for 6·4% leaves an unaccounted for loss of 0·2%.

These figures show that for every 100 kg crude fat 93·4 kg were obtained as finished deodorized fat. Of the 6·6 kg representing the shrinkage, 5·5 kg are recovered as by-product fatty matter of lower grades. The balance of 1·1 kg is explained by loss of moisture and coarse impurities, some loss of fatty matter in converting soap into acid oil and in wash-water, loss of fatty matter in extracted bleaching adsorbent and in water from the condensers. An unaccounted-for loss of 0·2 kg may be due to plant leakages, oil absorbed in filter cloth, difficulties in sampling for analytical purposes, etc.

THURMAN[123] has published some results of analyses of refining losses from industrial experience in U.S.A. arising from impurities in the crude oil purchased and in various process steps. They do not include the loss of fatty matter in the form of soap, which varies, of course, with the percentage of free fatty acids in the crude oil. THURMAN's figures are given in Table IX.

Regular process control by weighing or gauging of the fat at progressive stages, preferably as crude, neutralized and deodorized fat, and by similar checks on by-products, backed by chemical analyses, help to focus attention on process efficiency. Accidental losses of material can be minimized by the installation of adequately dimensioned fat-traps in all effluent systems.

In many refineries volume measurements are used instead of weighing. In such cases the temperature when measurements take place must be noted

182

TABLE IX

	Cottonseed Oil (%)	Corn Oil (%)	Groundnut Oil (%)	Soya Bean Oil (%)	Coconut Oil (%)
Moisture and impurities	0·38	0·38	0·38	0·38	0·43
Phosphatides and gums	0·76	—	0·3	0·5	0·2
Loss of fatty matter in emulsions	0·15	—	0·15	0·15	0·075
Glycerine loss from saponification	0·08	—	0·04	0·04	0·06
Fatty matter soluble in water	—	—	—	—	0·07
„ „ lost in bleaching	0·45	0·45	0·45	0·45	0·24
„ „ lost in deodorizing	0·25	0·55	0·25	0·55	0·45

and differences in specific gravity allowed for. The wide range of temperatures at which oils and fats are treated at different stages makes the use of actual weighing at certain stages highly commendable.

It is useful for process control purposes to compare the amount of alkali used with the amount theoretically required for neutralization of the oils and fats treated, each one of which must be dealt with separately owing to the different molecular weights of their mixed fatty acids. It is customary to use for coconut oil 206, palm kernel and babassu oils 220, palm oil 256, and for other fats and oils 282, i.e., the molecular weight of oleic acid. Thus for 1 ton free fatty acids in coconut oil 194 kg caustic soda (100 per cent) is required. The corresponding amounts for palm kernel and babassu oils are 182 kg, for palm oil 156 kg, and for other fats and oils based on oleic acid 142 kg. As an excess is practically always deliberately used, and as the neutralized fat is often given a caustic wash, the caustic soda factor, i.e., the ratio of caustic used to that theoretically required, is usually 1·3–1·5, and for some oils, where the lye is used also for colour reduction and for de-gumming (cottonseed oil, soya bean oil, etc.) factors as high as 3–4 are often found. Where the neutralizing chemicals are carbonate of soda or slaked lime other equivalents apply, and it is customary to convert these into the equivalent amount of caustic soda by multiplying the quantity of carbonate by 0·76 and the lime (CaO) by 1·43.

A routine statistical process control of the amount of bleaching material used is difficult to apply as there is considerable difference in the bleaching activity of the different brands and types of adsorbents, and even between different consignments. There are also often variations in response of different deliveries of the same type of oil to the same proportion of adsorbent. A record must, however, be kept of the amount of adsorbent added to each type of fat and of its moisture content, so that analyses of the fatty matter in the filterpress residue, ascertained as mentioned on page 129 and based on dry residue, will enable the loss of fat in the bleaching process to be correctly allocated.

Where recovered by-product fatty matter cannot be directly allotted to a particular batch or raw material as, for instance, from common drains and traps, the total should be allocated pro rata to the various qualities treated.

A regular system of records of stocks of materials and ingredients and of movements of these, coupled with appropriate chemical analyses, acts as a rapid and efficient check on process efficiency, and thus on cost. This is not only affected by the yields of finished product, but also by the degree of recovery and the value of the by-products, and by a number of items which are largely outside the control of the refinery management, such as wages and salaries, overhead expenses, cost of materials and ingredients, chemicals, filter cloths and papers, etc., repairs and maintenance. A fairly heavy item in the process cost is steam and other means of heating. If the heating is by steam only, the consumption of this, including steam for stripping, may be 1–2 tons of steam per ton of throughput. Much economy in this use of steam can be achieved by an extensive use of heat recovery in heat-exchangers, by collecting condensate, etc. A considerable proportion of the steam is used for heating water for washing neutralized fat in the batch process; the continuous neutralization process with wash centrifuges claims a considerable economy in this respect; but even refineries employing continuous processes and extensive heat recovery use 0·5–0·7 tons steam per ton input.

4

COMPLETE REFINERY PLANTS

MANY factors have to be considered in designing a refinery plant; not only must the weekly output be known, but also the number of different fats and oils to be treated and the quantity of each. The size and number of neutralizing vessels depend on whether these are to be used as neutralizer-bleachers or whether separate washing and bleaching vessels will be used. Decisions on methods of neutralizing may be influenced by methods of disposal and treatment of soapstock. Methods and conditions of deodorizing may depend on available means of heating and supplies of water for condensation. Total output and the number of different raw materials determine whether continuous methods can be considered.

Some examples of layouts of refinery plants are given in Figs. 89, 91, 92 and 95.

Fig. 89 shows the plan for a refinery designed by *Harburger Eisen- und Bronzewerke*, Germany, for treating batches of 10 tons. The various units are arranged on galleries round a light-well which permits easy supervision and control.

The system of operation in this plant is based on separate vessels for neutralization (open), washing and drying (closed, vacuum) and bleaching (horizontal, vacuum). Two deodorizers of smaller capacity (5 tons charge each) are connected to a common vacuum system, and cooling of the deodorized oil is done in external separate coolers. With time cycles of 6–8 hours in the various process vessels the capacity of the plant is about 30–40 tons per 24 hours.

While Fig. 90 shows the process flow chart, Fig. 89*a–e* shows the layout of the refinery. Pump *1* charges the open neutralizer *2* with crude oil. The neutralized oil is skimmed by vacuum to washing and drying vessel *3* and the soapstock is drained to soapstock tank *25*. The washed dried oil is drawn into the horizontal vacuum bleacher *4*. The oil-bleaching earth mixture after bleaching is pumped by pump *16* to frame filterpress *15*, of which there are two. The filtered oil runs to the intermediate tank *24* for bleached oil. From this tank oil in quantities of 5 tons is drawn by vacuum into deodorizers *5*, which have steam coils for heating and are supplied with superheated steam from superheaters *11* for stripping. The deodorizer vapours pass via fat-trap *9* to the barometric jet condenser *7*, non-condensable gases being removed by air pump *8*. Trapped fat from the vapours runs to collecting tank *10*. Deodorized oil is cooled under vacuum in coolers *6*.

14 is an oil-separator basin for wash-waters from *3*; *12* is a surface condenser and *13* an air pump for creating the vacuum in wash-vessel and bleacher. The cooled deodorized oil is given a final filtration by means of

185

Section *A–B*

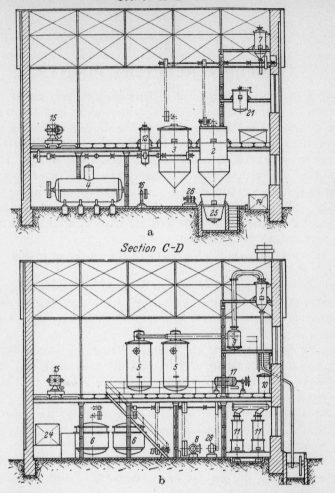

a

Section *C–D*

b

Fig. 89.   Refining plant, according to *Harburger Eisen- und Bronzewerke*)

pump *18* and filterpress (chamber press) *17*. *19*,*20*, *21* represent lye-dissolving tank, lye pump and lye-measuring tank for the neutralizer. *22* is a hot-water tank and *23* a tank for salt solution, both for use in connection with neutralization and washing. *26* is the pump for soapstock and *27* a common fat-trap tank for all effluents from the refinery.

A slightly different scheme is shown in Fig. 91 representing a plan by *Bamag Ltd.*, London. In this arrangement there is an open neutralizer (see Fig. 32), a combined washing and bleaching vacuum vessel (see Fig. 58) with ordinary barometric jet condenser vacuum arrangement, a filterpress for separating bleaching earth, a deodorizer (see Fig. 64) with high-vacuum equipment. Cooling of deodorized oil takes place in the deodorizer. Auxiliary plant comprises tanks for chemicals, measuring tank for these, soda dis-

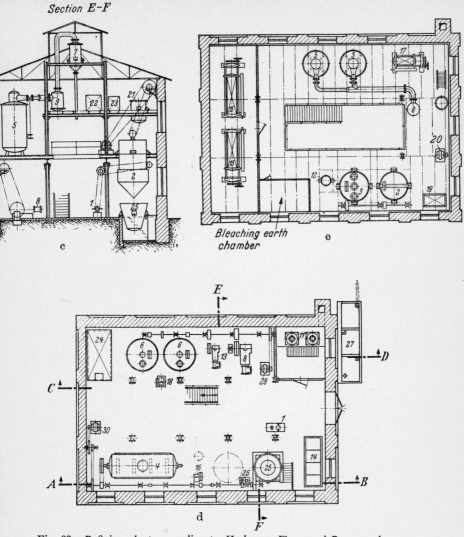

Section E-F

Bleaching earth
chamber

Fig. 89.—Refining plant, according to *Harburger Eisen- und Bronzewerke*.

solving tank, soapstock tank and pump, tank for cloudy oil from filtration, fatty acid separator trap in the deodorizer vapour line and receiving vessel for trapped material. There are also storage tanks for crude oil, bleached oil and deodorized oil. The equipment in this refinery deals with batches of 10 tons each in the first step and 12 tons for deodorizing. The capacity of the plant per 24 hours is about 30–35 tons.

In Fig. 92 (*a–e*) the plan shows in addition to the refinery plant also the plant for treatment and recovery of by-products. Fig. 93 is a process flow chart for this refinery indicating also pipe connections.

Fig. 92 shows floor plans and sections through the building. The layout

187

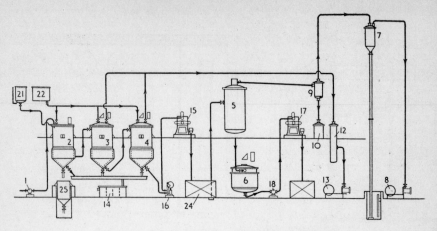

Fig. 90.   Process flow-sheet for refinery in Fig. 89.

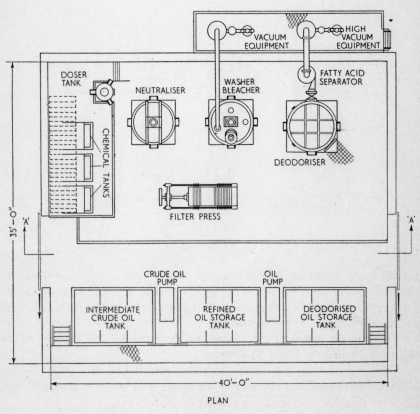

Fig. 91.   Refinery plant—plan (Courtesy: *Bamag, Ltd., London*).

provides a neutralizer-bleacher of an appropriate size, from which bleached oil after filtration reaches a buffer storage tank for supplying bleached oil to the deodorizers. The deodorized oil is cooled in the deodorizers before final filtration. Superheated steam is used for stripping, boiler steam for heating purposes. The by-products plant comprises vessels for settling soap-stock for recovery of enmeshed neutral oil and for splitting soapstock with sulphuric acid.

The crude oil from tank *1* is conveyed by compressed air to neutralizer-bleacher *2*, where it is neutralized, washed and bleached; the vacuum for drying and bleaching in this vessel is drawn by pump *22*. *3* is a buffer storage for bleached oil, *4* the two deodorizers, each of half the capacity of the neutralizer. *5* is the condenser, *23* the high-vacuum pump for the deodorizer vacuum plant. *6*, *7*, *8* and *9* are dissolving tank, pressure vessel, overhead tank and measuring tank for caustic soda, *10* a hot-water tank, *11* a salt-water tank, all for use in connection with the neutralizer. Soapstock is drained into tank *12*, and any emulsions, which may be formed, into tank *13*, where they are broken with salt water and steam.

Bleached oil is forced by compressed air, produced by compressor *20*,

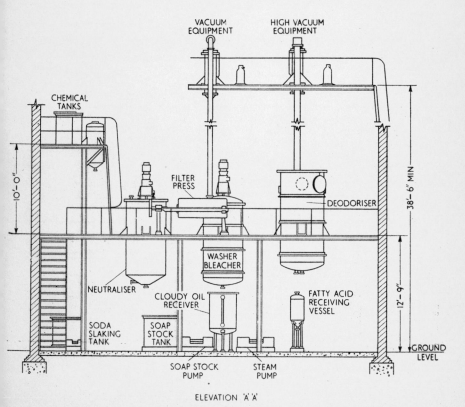

ELEVATION 'A' 'A'

Fig. 91.—Refinery plant—elevation (Courtesy: *Bamag, Ltd., London*).

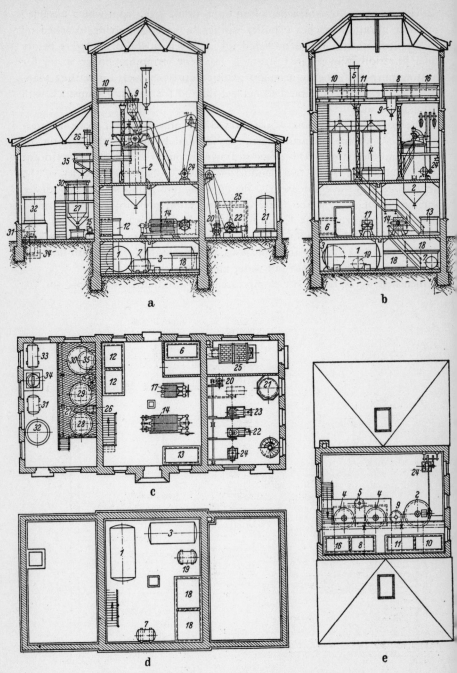

Fig. 92. Refinery plant, according to *Bamag-Meguin A.G.*

through frame filterpress *14* and separated from bleaching earth. Pump *15* transports soapstock from the tank under the neutralizer either to overhead tank *16* or direct to the splitting-tank *30*.

The deodorized cooled oil from *4* is blank-filtered in chamber press *17*

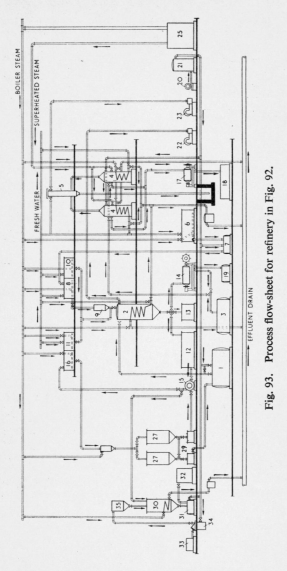

Fig. 93.   Process flow-sheet for refinery in Fig. 92.

and run to tank *18* for finished oil. Any cloudy oil from first runnings from filterpress *14* is collected in *19* and re-filtered.

25 is the superheater for stripping steam. In the same wing of the building are compressor *20* and air vessel *21*, the two vacuum pumps *22* and *23* and motor *24*. On the opposite side of the building (Fig. 92*a* and *c*) is the plant for

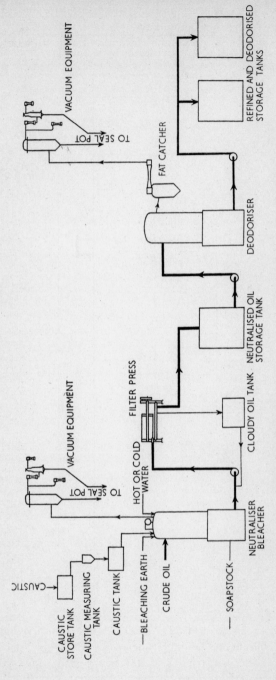

Fig. 94. Flow diagram for refinery (Courtesy : *W. J. Fraser & Co. Ltd., Dagenham*).

1. NEUTRALISER—BLEACHER.
2. NEUTRALISER VACUUM EQUIPMENT.
3. DEODORISER.
4. FAT CATCHER.
5. DEODORISER VACUUM EQUIPMENT.
6. FILTER PRESSES.
7. BUFFER TANKS.
8. REFINED OIL TANKS.
9. OIL DRUM HEATER.
10. DECANTED CRUDE OIL TANK.
11. MELTED OIL TANK
12. SETTLING TANK.
13. HOT WATER WASH TANK
14. CLOUDY OIL TANK.
15. WEIGH TANKS.
16. CAUSTIC DISSOLVER.
17. STRONG CAUSTIC TANKS.
18. CAUSTIC MEASURING TANKS.
19. CAUSTIC TANKS.
20. BLEACHING EARTH HOPPER.
21. AIR COMPRESSOR.
22. PUMPS.
23. PROCESS HOT WATER TANK.
24. PROCESS COLD WATER TANK.
25. WEIGH SCALE

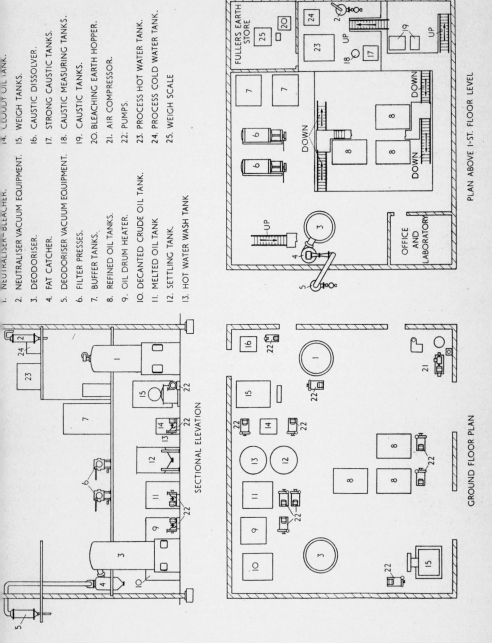

PLAN ABOVE I-ST. FLOOR LEVEL

SECTIONAL ELEVATION

GROUND FLOOR PLAN

Fig. 95. Lay-out of refinery (Courtesy: *W. J. Fraser & Co. Ltd., Dagenham*).

193

soap splitting, consisting of soapstock settling tanks *27* where enmeshed neutral oil may be recovered from soapstock and collected in *29* and returned to crude oil tank *1*, splitting-tank *30* for acid oil production from soapstock by acidulation with sulphuric acid from acid store-tank *33*, pressure vessel *34* and measuring vessel *35*. *30* is also used for washing the acid oil, which after washing free from mineral acid runs to pressure vessel *31* and is blown by compressed air to storage tank *32*.

The capacity of this plant, if the neutralizer-bleacher deals with batches of 12–15 tons, would be about 30 tons per 24 hours.

Fig. 94 shows a flow diagram for the refinery laid out according to the plan in Fig. 95 by *Messrs W. J. Fraser & Co. Ltd.*, Dagenham, Essex. The refining system is based on the use of a neutralizer-bleacher (see Fig. 33), which during bleaching is operated under vacuum, provided by a quick-starting ejector and afterwards by a 2-stage steam jet ejector, but no aug-mentor. Cloudy oil from the filterpress is re-circulated for repeated filtration, whereas clear bleached oil runs to a buffer storage tank, from which the high-vacuum deodorizer is supplied as required. This deodorizer is of the con-struction shown in Fig. 65, and the augmentor and condenser vacuum system as shown in Fig. 80.

Fig. 95 shows the layout of this refinery, which is housed in a building of light construction and arranged on two floors. Both neutralizer-bleacher and deodorizer are supported on bases on the ground floor and reach through into the upper floor. The base for the neutralizer-bleacher contains the draining tanks for soapstock and washings. If the process vessels are con-structed for working charges of 10 tons the weekly output can be about 120 tons. Crude fats, if solid, are melted in heater *9*, clarified in tank *10* and stored in tank *11*. To check quantities during processing there are weigh-tanks *15*. The soapstock from neutralizing is disposed of as such, emulsions and wash-waters are settled in tanks *12* and *13*. Cloudy oil from filterpresses *6* is collected in tank *14* for re-filtration. *7* are buffer tanks for semi-processed oil. The deodorized oil is stored in tanks *8*. Caustic soda is dissolved in tank *16* and pumped up as strong lye to tank *17* and measured out in tank *18* for dilution in service tanks *19*. On the upper floor is a partitioned-off store for bleaching earth, which is weighed off on scale *25* and drawn into the bleacher from hopper *20*. On the elevated platform on the first floor are service tanks *23* and *24* for hot and cold water, as well as the storage tank for strong caustic; this platform also gives access to the vacuum equipment for the neutralizer-bleacher. The plans show a number of service pumps *22* and an air compressor *21*. The first floor is built as a gallery round the walls, leaving a light-well in the middle of the building.

Since the development during the last fifteen years of continuous neutraliza-tion processes, and the recent improvements in continuous deodorizers, combinations of continuous and batch processes have been increasingly used in a number of refineries.

The first continuous plant to be used on industrial scale was the early type of continuous deodorizer (see p. 155) which dealt with batch-neutralized and bleached oil.

The continuous neutralization plants, using caustic soda or carbonate of soda as described on pp. 58, 62 and 74, are so far mostly working in conjunction with batch deodorizers. The neutralization plants illustrated in Figs. 36, 38 and 45, deliver a dried neutral oil to storage vessels, from which it is drawn as required to the bleachers, which are usually of the vacuum bleacher type. Although during the last few years some continuous bleaching processes have been developed (see pp. 122–124) they have not yet found wide application, but whether continuous or batch bleaching processes are used, the bleached oil should be delivered to buffer storage tanks, as subsequent deodorizing, batch as well as continuous, cannot usually be synchronized in time schedule with bleaching owing to the varying response of different oils and fats to both bleaching and deodorizing.

The space occupied by continuous plants is not significantly smaller than that needed for batch plants. A continuous neutralization plant is usually arranged on one floor, apart from service vessels, whereas batch neutralizers are tall vessels often projecting through one or more floors. Bleaching and filtration plants, whether for batch or continuous operation, are of similar type and dimensions. Continuous deodorizers of the column type are taller, but of smaller diameter than batch deodorizers with equal output.

Auxiliary plant, such as storage tanks for crude, intermediary and final products, service tanks and equipment for chemicals and hot water, tanks for by-products and their treatment, pumps, vacuum and condensation plant, etc., is essentially the same for different types of plant of similar capacity. Continuous plants make more extensive use of heat-exchangers and control by instrumentation.

Although it is reported that some installations exist in which neutralization and bleaching are continuous and deodorization semi-continuous or continuous, each of these steps operate on independent time schedules. The majority of installations can be classified as being one of the following types:

   i. Batch operations only.

   ii. Continuous neutralization, buffer storage, batch bleaching, buffer storage, batch deodorization.

   iii. Batch neutralization, batch bleaching, buffer storage, continuous or semi-continuous deodorization.

   iv. Continuous neutralization, buffer storage, batch bleaching, buffer storage, continuous or semi-continuous deodorization.

As examples of comparative requirements of the principal plant units for these schemes, based on a throughput of 60 tons per 24 hours, the following combinations may serve as guide. Auxiliary plant common to all schemes, as well as minor items, are omitted.

   1. 3 × 10-ton neutralizer-bleachers, filtration plant, buffer storage tanks, 2 × 10-ton deodorizers, 1 × 10-ton cooler for deodorized oil. If the

quantities of the different crude materials vary much, it may be advantageous to have 2 × 10-ton and 2 × 5-ton neutralizer-bleachers and 1 × 10-ton and 2 × 5-ton deodorizers. It is assumed that the deodorizers can be operated under an abs. pressure of 6 mm.

If the refiner prefers to carry out the neutralization, washing and bleaching processes in separate vessels, an arrangement as shown in Fig. 89 can be used. Open vessels can be employed for neutralizing and washing, but if the wash-vessel is also to be used for drying the contents prior to bleaching it must be connected to the vacuum system. As, however, the bleaching process requires much less time than neutralizing and washing, there is usually ample time for the drying to be done in the bleacher. Many refiners prefer to commence the bleaching while a trace of moisture is still present in the oil.

2. 4 neutralization or primary centrifuges with sludge discharge, 4 re-refine centrifuges, 2 sets of 3 wash-centrifuges, appropriate proportioning and mixing plant, vacuum dryer (Sharples system, Fig. 36), buffer storage tanks, 2 × 6-ton vacuum bleachers, filtration plant, buffer storage tanks, 2 × 10-ton deodorizers, 1 × 10-ton cooler for deodorized oil.

If the continuous neutralization plant is of the De Laval type (see Fig. 38), or of the Clayton carbonate-process type (see Fig. 45), the number of centrifuges is slightly different owing to different capacity of the individual machines.

3. 3 × 10-ton neutralizer-bleachers, filtration plant, buffer storage tanks, 2 continuous deodorizers for 1·5 tons per hour, equipped with continuous coolers, or 1 semi-continuous deodorizer for 2·5 tons per hour. Special heater for the deodorizers.

4. Neutralization plant as in 2, buffer storage tanks, bleaching plant as in 2, filtration plant, buffer storage tanks, 2 continuous deodorizers for 1·5 tons per hour, equipped with continuous coolers, or 1 semi-continuous deodorizer for 2·5 tons per hour. Special heater for the deodorizers.

5
STATISTICAL INFORMATION

THE development of the industry of refining fats and oils for edible purposes was the sequence to the change in the pattern of society following the industrial revolution in the nineteenth century. The migration of a large part of the population from the country and farming to the towns and industry demanded the transfer of raw materials for fatty foods from places of abundant production to, frequently, distant places of consumption. To eliminate the results of deterioration caused by storage and transport of the fatty raw materials and to render the fats more attractive to the Western palate the refining industry was gradually built up, until it has now become one of the largest food industries. Some indication of its magnitude can be gleaned from the figures in Table X, which show the estimated consumption in a number of countries of edible fats and oils which have undergone full refining treatment, as for use in margarine, cooking fats, shortenings and confectionery fats, or complete or partial refining as for cooking oils, salad oils, etc. The figures give the pre-war consumption for 1938 or, in some cases, the

TABLE X

Country	Pre-war	1949	1950
United Kingdom	358,500	641,500	634,000
Belgium	68,000	69,500	77,500
France	164,000	135,000	158,000
Holland	85,000	157,000	177,000
Denmark	73,000	52,500	56,500
Norway	51,000	55,500	60,000
Sweden	55,500	63,500	73,500
Germany	528,500	294,000 (Western)	437,500 Western)
U.S.A.	1,200,000	1,501,000	1,698,000
Canada	62,500	88,000	118,000
South Africa	12,000	19,500	20,000
India and Pakistan	41,000	166,500	182,000
Australia	19,500	25,000	28,500

197

average for 4–5 years immediately before the war and the estimated consumptions in 1949 and 1950 in metric tons. Butterfat, lard, suet and some other animal fats are not included, though some of these may have been partly refined.

In addition very large quantities of vegetable oils are consumed in India and Pakistan (about 925,000 tons in 1950), a considerable part of which has been more or less refined. Important refining industries also exist in Italy, Switzerland, Argentine, Brazil, Indonesia and several other countries. As the total butter consumption in 1950 was estimated to be about 2,500,000 tons and the consumption of ghee in India and Pakistan about 600,000 tons, it will be seen from the figures quoted that the refining of edible fats and oils is probably the largest edible fat industry. And in addition there is a considerable industry also in Russia and other Communist countries from which statistical information is not available.

SUBJECT INDEX

199